UPPING YOUR STEP

TRAINING FOR SUCCESS IN IRISH DANCING

PubliBook IRELAND

ISBN: 978-1-909774-25-4

Published in 2016 by **PubliBook Ireland**
5 Cranbrooke – The Grange – Newcastle Road – Lucan, Co. Dublin, Ireland

A CIP Catalogue record for this book is available from
The British Library and the Irish Copyright Libraries.

Designed, typeset, printed and bound in Ireland by **PubliBook Ireland**

www.publibookireland.com

UPPING YOUR STEP

TRAINING FOR SUCCESS IN IRISH DANCING

PETER O'GRADY

DISCLAIMER

This book will provide you with helpful information which you can use when you are taking part in Irish dancing training. It contains advice in relation to health and fitness. It is important to remember that in all sports, conditioning programmes and nutritional information can pose a risk to your health and fitness. Therefore, the author wants to make it clear that you need to take full personal responsibility when using any of the information he has provided. Before you put into practice any of the suggestions in this book, it is recommended that you check with a health professional to make sure that it is safe for you. If you decide to use any training equipment, make sure it is well-maintained. Do not take risks and train above your level of fitness. The information in this book has been collected by the author himself. It sets out his own thoughts and provides you with knowledge based on his own training and coaching experience. As this is one of the first Irish dancing health and fitness-related books of its kind, the information provided is not intended to be a definitive set of instructions for this activity.

The book is designed to provide as much information as possible to Irish dancers, young and old, male and female, all across the globe. Therefore, I recommend that you learn as much as possible from this book, and use it to your advantage, but make sure that you tailor it to your own individual needs.

The author has done everything to make sure that the information in this book is accurate, as he hopes you, the reader, will succeed in your efforts. While there may be some suggestions that you disagree with, you should use this book as a general guide rather than a complete source of information.

The author will not take responsibility or assume liability for any person or entity with respect to loss, damage or injuries caused, or allegedly caused, directly or indirectly by the information provided in this book.

DEDICATION

To my partner, who has supported me and listened to my crazy ideas over these past few years, and to our children who have distracted me from writing this book time and time again, I thank you. You were my motivators and the reason why I completed this book.

I would also like to thank my parents, brothers, sister and extended family for their support over the years. You're the best. You have helped me to grow as a person, and you have always been there for me when times were good, but more importantly, when times were hard. I dedicate a great deal of my success to you.

ACKNOWLEDGMENTS

I would like to begin by saying that, until now, I did not have any history as a writer. I am a sports physical therapist and a strength and conditioning coach who loves all aspects of health, fitness and training. My experience and love of my work, and of Irish dancing in particular, has helped me develop into a writer. This book has given me the opportunity to put in writing all the knowledge I have gathered and everything I have been teaching my dance students over the past few years.

I would like to dedicate this book to my family, without whom I would not have accomplished what I have achieved today. A special word of thanks to my granny, Elizabeth McNeice, who passed away recently and never got to see the publication of this book.

Thanks everyone for all the support through the ups and downs, for the help you gave me throughout my sporting career, for encouraging me and my crazy ideas and for believing in me always.

I would like to thank Paul Ruttledge for the enormous effort he put into the cover design and illustrations. We have been friends since we were five years of age. Watching your work throughout the years, I knew you would be the perfect artist for my book.

I would also like to thank you, the readers. By choosing this book you have shown your support. I hope, in turn, it will assist you to reach your own goals. I look forward to working with you in the future.

Thank you everyone,
Peter O'Grady

ABOUT THE AUTHOR

Peter O'Grady is one of the only strength and conditioning coaches in Ireland who works with Irish dancers. He has spent the last three years travelling Ireland, conducting workshops and seminars, visiting schools and providing one-to-one training to help dancers prepare for big competitions. He has now also begun to offer an online support service, working with dancers from all over the world, through his website www.irishdancingphysicalfitness.com.

Peter was an Irish dancer himself for many years, competing in the Connacht, All-Ireland and World Irish Dancing Championships. He has gained many qualifications in the last few years, including strength and conditioning coaching, and sports physical therapy and nutrition, as well as lecturing in fitness instruction. He has a huge passion for health and fitness and demonstrates this on a daily basis in his very own training facility, The Unit Gym and CrossFit, which is based in Claregalway, Co. Galway, Ireland.

Peter always had a huge interest in the activities he took part in, including Irish dancing, Gaelic football, soccer and Judo. Unfortunately, he got injured at a young age and was forced to stop competing. He tried his best to recover, and sought the advice of many surgeons and physiotherapists. However, he was unsuccessful in finding the solution he needed. It was at this point that he decided he wanted to help others to stay fit, healthy and injury-free. Peter began by attending various courses, during which he used the knowledge he had learned to help recover from his own injuries. Since then, he has remained injury-free and the injury he had is no longer a problem.

Peter always wanted to do something other than working in the usual 9 to 5 job. He was constantly aiming for something better and always setting himself a goal to achieve. When he finished his courses and started working with dancers, he really wanted to make a change to the Irish dancing world, by providing them with information that most dancers have never received before. He decided to write this book, as he wanted to share his knowledge with other Irish dancers, as well as a wider audience.

It is clear that fitness and health will play a huge part in Irish dancing in the future. Peter is highly committed and dedicated to sport. As well as running a gym facility, he hopes to one day work with dancers from around the world, on a regular basis, dedicating his time to helping them achieve their goals and make their dreams come true.

PETER O'GRADY

A MESSAGE FROM PETER

My journey began when I was just seven years of age. I put on my first pair of dancing shoes, which were in fact ugly, black and flat soled. My two brothers, Brendan who was older than me, and Paul who was younger, had both started dancing before me and I swore that I wouldn't dance myself. My cousin, who was a world champion, started dancing at the age of three and by this stage was already dancing for two years. My mother, aunts and uncles all danced at some point in their lives. So I suppose it was our generation's turn to at least give it a try.

I was sure that my first dancing class would also be my last. The teacher was really delighted to have boys in her school, but I wished I felt the same. After the first class ended I was still unsure, but I did make an effort to continue to attend, to give myself the chance to see if I would begin to enjoy it.

Within the space of a few weeks, we had changed dance school. A few months later again I was competing, and before I knew it, by eight years of age I was enrolled in an advanced dance class. My older brother Brendan had quit at this stage, but my younger brother Paul kept it up for a little while longer. I will never forget my first advanced dance class. I was very shy and I didn't know any of the other dancers. I was sitting on the other side of the room to everyone else and all I had for lunch was a juice drink and a packet of sweets.... not to be recommended! As the class went on, I got to know some of the other dancers, whom I am still friends with to this day. Gradually, I began to feel more comfortable and I started to enjoy it. Not long after that, I found myself dancing on the podium at the Connacht Irish Dancing Championships, continuing on to the All-Ireland Championships and then finally qualifying for the World Championships.

This experience taught me the importance of patience, and that you should never give up on anything too quickly. Success is something you work for, it is not something that happens to you. Many of you reading this may not have reached your dream of becoming a podium dancer, or taking part in a dancing championship, but that does not mean you are not a winner. A winner is somebody who gives it their all; somebody who has worked hard to get to where they are. A winner doesn't give up because they get a poor result. Instead, they keep pushing forward, despite receiving knocks along the way. If you do this, you are already a champion! If you do this in life, you will be successful.

This book aims to give every dancer the chance to become the best that they can be. To do this, you must focus on the areas that need most attention, and not ignore them by only concentrating on what you do best. In doing so, you are taking control of your weaknesses. Also, make sure to build your self-confidence and self-belief, and do not let anyone put you down. If you read the information I have given you and put these simple tips into practice, then you will become the best dancer you can be.

Peter O'Grady

CONTENTS

./..

INTRODUCTION

The system I have designed in this book is based on my own experience as a sports physical therapist and also as a strength and conditioning coach. I have had the opportunity to witness the human body perform through all angles of the physical spectrum. I have seen athletic accomplishments, as well as some struggles in recuperation and rehabilitation. This book has evolved from my knowledge, mistakes and successes. I have been on a quest to develop a model to refine conditioning, injury prevention, improve performance and to simplify a training method for Irish dancers. Following hours of study, I finally came up with the solution, and can now provide you with answers to your problems in relation to dance steps. You will see how I have described the common problems in dance performances and I have explained how to improve on these areas, using simple exercises.

Irish dancing, as we all know, is an extraordinary display of physical skill that becomes an art and a charming delight to observe. It requires intense muscular control, speed, stamina, balance, rhythm and elegance. In order to be able to compete in today's high performance market, you must be both physically and mentally fit. The need to impress audiences, judges, parents and teachers has never been more evident. Newly updated choreography and a dancer's display of perfection are now needed to win competitions.

Dance schools are busy places, where rehearsals are constantly taking place, and competitions are held weekly. As a dancer, you are working harder than ever, trying to perform the steps to the best of your ability. Dance techniques have been passed down from generation to generation, with very little attention paid to anatomical analysis. While this may have been the case and it worked well in the past, in order to gain an edge in competitions nowadays, you must be familiar with basic anatomy, and really understand how the body works to improve on your own dancing technique.

Upping Your Step will assist you in discovering more efficient ways to improve your performance. This is different from other strength and conditioning books in that it specifically focuses on Irish dancers. Another unique factor is that this is the first book to explain the real reasons behind poor performances in relation to dancing techniques. I believe that in order to successfully build capacity to attain the highest level of achievement and to reach your own capabilities, I recommend that you approach your training in the same way as an athlete. To do this, you will need to understand how your body works mechanically, the function of each muscle group, and how they specifically relate to Irish dancing movements. This book provides you with a full understanding of the interrelationship between each muscle group and the fine movements of the body involved in dancing. The images demonstrating each exercise will give you an understanding of movement, the muscles that contract to create an action, and how and why these movements underperform. I explain in detail the exercises you must carry out, on a daily basis, in order to improve specific dance movements.

You may have seen your friends, family or perhaps some random dancers using exercises that you have never seen before and you think that they will be beneficial to you. This is not always the case. This book will provide the tools needed for effective results and will give you the answers to your own individual problems. You will be more confident in your training and programme plan.

The steps along your journey must be executed in the proper sequence. It involves doing what is necessary on a daily basis to progress forward and attain conditioning goals. This book presents efficient and effective methods for enhancing your performance and it will guide you through the training process.

CHAPTER 1
BACK TO THE BASICS

Before we begin, I thought it might be helpful to discuss some of the basics.

Firstly, training should be progressive. A baby cannot run before it walks. Your training should grow gradually, in the same way as a baby develops. You will have days where you think that you could have worked harder or you could have done more repetitions. However, as the days go on, your body will be introduced to greater amounts of stress, so you must be patient until you reach these stages.

DO NOT OVERLOAD YOUR BODY BY TRAINING TOO QUICKLY

Secondly, training must be designed to progress towards a particular time or event. When we train, we need to know that we are preparing for something specific. When we have a big event ahead of us, we want to be sure that we have followed the steps and stages correctly. We need to put arrangements in place so that we can build on these continuously, in the same way as a baby grows, before reaching the final date or event.

HAVE A TRAINING PLAN

Thirdly, good training requires vision. A vision sets out how you will progress from crawling, to walking, to running, and then to sprinting. It does not matter how hard or how easy the task may be, you must believe that completing the steps and stages correctly will eventually lead to success.

BELIEVE IN YOUR TRAINING PLAN!

Finally, training requires that a physical load be disbursed across a period of time to allow growth and development to complete the task ahead of you. You must believe in your training, as well as your training programme. You will not see the end result until the event itself, so trust your training. You must follow your plan effectively and efficiently.

FOLLOW YOUR TRAINING PLAN AND YOU WILL ACCOMPLISH

MAXINE SPELMAN

CHAPTER 2
UNDERSTANDING PAIN AND DISCOMFORT

It is very important that you understand pain and discomfort and they must be taken seriously. The saying 'no pain no gain' can sometimes be misinterpreted. This does not mean that you continue to dance or train, if you are feeling pain or discomfort from an injury, be it old or new. Instead, the saying usually means that it is more than likely to be beneficial, if you are pushing yourself to your limits, whilst performing a strength exercise, to get the steps absolutely perfect or to get that extra rep (to feel the burn).

What is the first thing you should do when you feel pain? Stop! The body is smart. It will give you signals that something is not right and usually when you are in pain this means something is wrong. You should not continue to perform any type of exercise that puts extra pressure on a possible injury.

This brings to mind when my car broke down some time ago when driving home from Belfast. The oil light and engine management light came on together on the dashboard, which is never a good sign. To make a long story short, I had to get a taxi the rest of the journey home and my car had to be fixed at a nearby garage. The point I am making is, when we see something wrong with our vehicles, why do we fix the problem straight away? On the other hand, when we are in pain we feel that we can work through it. Usually in these situations we escalate the problem. It may start out at first as something small, but if you do nothing about it, it becomes a bigger problem. You dance through it again and again and again. Instead of stopping, you continue to dance or exercise. Eventually you purchase medication or some other pain relief products such as an ice pack, muscle rubs or neoprene sleeves until your next class, thinking this will solve the problem. Covering up the pain or trying to fix it temporarily will only cause more damage. Buying medication and ice packs tells me that the pain is so bad that you want it to go away so you can dance properly again, but by denying it you are ignoring one of the important steps to perfecting your performance.

Missing dance practice or a Feis (an Irish dance competition) is always heart-breaking. In these situations, we would do anything to be able to perform. Scientists today have come up with several ways to mask the problem, which enables you to do this. However, you must be aware that this is only a temporary solution and it is important to know that the pain is trying to tell you something. There could be many reasons for this pain, such as:

- You did not warm up correctly.
- You did not stretch properly, or you are using the wrong stretching techniques.
- Your posture is not correct.
- You had poor form and/or technique.
- You have a muscle imbalance.
- You have an old injury that you never looked after properly, when it first occurred.
- It may not be related to exercise at all. It may be something even more serious.

Use pain to your advantage. Go through this checklist and work out what might have caused your pain. Your warm-up may have been too intense, too soon. Your stretching techniques may be incorrect, or you could be using unsuitable stretches at the wrong time. Maybe you have to adjust your posture. Are you moving the way your dance teacher would like? Are you pushing yourself to fatigue, resulting in poor form and technique, which is causing injury? Is it an old injury, or is it something else? These are questions you need to ask yourself. Many of these small steps may fix your problem and prevent it from reoccurring. If your injury is already showing signs of inflammation and swelling, then you will not be able to work on your form and technique. You must rest instead. The bottom line is that you must fix the problem before you can perform again. In order to do this, you must try to find out why it occurred in the first place and correct it. In doing this, you have less chance of the same injury reoccurring.

CHAPTER 3
INJURY AND RECOVERY

While injuries may be easy to recognise, they may have underlying factors that are sometimes not as simple as they might first appear.

Athletes, in general, can overtrain at times. They train and compete beyond their limits at every practice session causing pain, stiffness, soreness or even injury. If the injury is a simple strain, general muscle soreness or illness, and the athlete now wants to return to training, they should not do so without first discovering and understanding the cause of their problem. When they do this, they can begin by returning to some light activity exercise called active recovery. This will help to alleviate soreness and tension and it will also prepare the body for higher intensity training in the future.

Active recovery will help you to maintain a certain level of fitness and can save time in the recovery process, but it should never be confused with rest. If you return too quickly to performing low intensity exercises, then no amount of medication or supplements will help you, and recovery will be much slower. Also, make sure that when you are ready to begin active recovery, that you do not mistakenly engage in moderate or high intensity training, as this can set you back again to the rest period.

Here are forms of active recovery which you can build into your programme. Remember to perform these exercises at a very low intensity level.

STATIONARY BIKE

Almost everyone has seen a rugby player on the side of the pitch, with an ice pack on a specific injury and cycling at low intensity on a stationary bike. This is done to increase his or her circulation by cycling, while also at the same time controlling any inflammation by placing an ice pack on the injured area.

The stationary bike is a simple exercise that can be used to increase circulation, but it should not be performed at a high level of intensity. Make sure that you do not remain in a stationary position, and that you do not continue to hold onto the handlebars. Sit upright on the bike, change position regularly by crossing your arms. Turn your upper body left to right and perform arm movement exercises, whilst keeping your spine in a comfortable position.

When you have completed 10–12 minutes of cycling, take a rest and perform stretching exercises, making sure to stretch the muscles that need most attention.

HOW DO I KNOW IF I AM CYCLING AT LOW INTENSITY?

Your breathing will be rapid, but you will still be able to hold a full conversation without running out of breath. If you are out of breath whilst having a conversation, then you will know that you are working too hard.

HIKING

While it depends on your level of fitness, walking is usually not enough for an Irish dancer who is trying to recover. You will need to increase your activity level a little bit more than with walking alone, but you still must avoid impact, fatigue and, of course, high intensity training.

Hiking can be one of the most intense forms of recovery. Make sure that you are familiar with the route you are taking and be confident that the course you choose will not have any negative effect on your recovery. Hiking requires a slightly greater range of motion than just normal walking. Therefore it is an excellent form of active stretching, and it also develops postural awareness. When planning a hike, make sure to bring a friend, some water, a healthy snack and dress appropriately.

TREADING WATER

Swimming is another form of active recovery, but most athletes and young people find it too strenuous because of their lack of experience and poor technique. However, most people are more than capable of treading water (swimming in a vertical position, while keeping your head over the surface of the water).

If you cannot tread water, you should wear a lifejacket or use a small floatation device that barely keeps you above water. You can then use your arms and legs to keep you afloat. As you become more proficient, you can use less floatation and more arm and leg movements. When you are capable of treading water without the support of a life jacket or small floatation, set a goal to be able to do this activity for up to 20 minutes, taking breaks and stretching, when necessary. When treading water you should try to stay relaxed and do as little as possible, whilst remaining afloat. Deep breathing and slow movements will allow you to conserve energy and maintain a low level of exercise.

CHAPTER 4
FOUNDATIONS OF EFFECTIVE TRAINING

I have designed this book to improve an Irish dancer's performance in the safest and most effective way. In gyms and health clubs around the world, the typical workout consists of isolation movements and extended aerobic sessions. The fitness community, from trainers to magazines, has convinced the exercising public that lateral raises, leg extensions, sit-ups, and other similar movements, combined with 20–40 minute stints on a stationary bike or treadmill will lead to great fitness levels. However, I prefer to work with dance-specific movements and shorter high-intensity cardiovascular sessions. I have replaced leg extensions with squats, and for every long-distance effort, my dancers will instead do five or six short-distance efforts at a higher intensity. Why? It is because functional movements and high-intensity intervals are radically more effective for an Irish dancer.

This is not a matter of opinion, but it is based on solid, irrefutable scientific fact. Yet the marginally effective, old ways still persist and are almost universal.

YOUR CURRENT REGIMEN

If your current routine looks somewhat similar to what is typically described in fitness magazines and gyms, do not despair. Any exercise is better than none, and you have not wasted your time. In fact, the aerobic exercises that you have been doing are an essential foundation to fitness and the isolation movements have given you some degree of strength. You are in good company. I have found that some of the world's best athletes were sorely lacking in building their core strength and conditioning. It is hard to believe that many elite athletes have achieved international success, but they are still far from reaching their full potential because they have not had the benefit of state-of-the-art coaching methods.

AN IRISH DANCER IS AN ATHLETE

When I state that 'Irish dancers are athletes', some people disagree, while others respect my viewpoint. I believe that an athlete is a person who is trained or skilled in strength, power, speed, balance, agility, flexibility and endurance, all of which are requirements demanded of an Irish dancer. This supports my claim that Irish dancers are indeed athletes. I wanted to make this point in my book because I speak with others who would have a different opinion, but when I explain my reasons for stating why I think Irish dancers are athletes they later agree.

CHAPTER 5
SCALE YOUR HEALTH AND PERFORMANCE

It is important to measure your health and performance. The method I use would be of great interest and benefit to dancers and teachers all around the world. Figure 5.1 below sets out health and performance scales. These scales can be used to calculate almost every measurable value related to health and can be graded from 1–10.

FIGURE 5.1: HEALTH AND PERFORMANCE SCALES

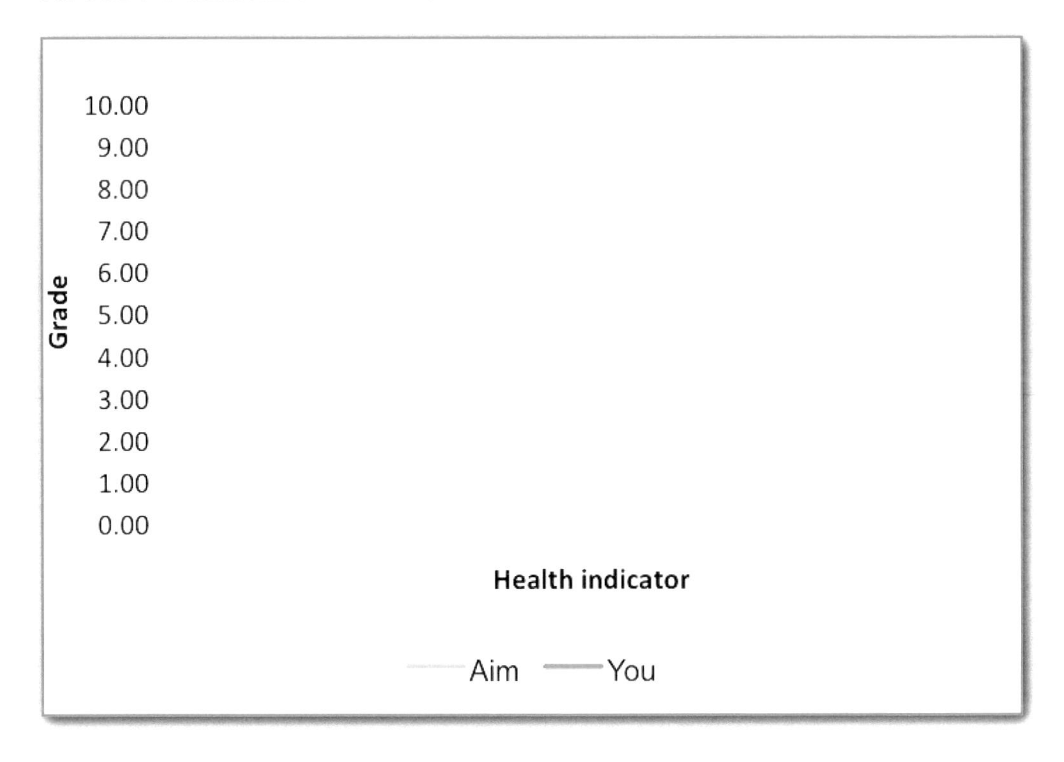

WHAT SHOULD YOU INCLUDE ON YOUR HEALTH AND PERFORMANCE SCALES?

Firstly, your measurements should be based on your blood pressure, body fat, body mass, bone density, cholesterol levels, muscle mass, flexibility, balance and so on.

For example, it can be used to scale your blood pressure, as shown in Table 5.1 below.

TABLE 5.1: SCALES TO MEASURE BLOOD PRESSURE

BLOOD PRESSURE READING	SCALE
160/90	0–3 (0=lowest result possible)
120/80 (normal or healthy)	4–7
110/60 (athlete's blood pressure)	8–10 (10=best possible result)

Other sample measurements that should be included on your health scales are diet, sleep, flexibility, strength, cardiovascular levels and so on. You will then become more like an athlete and you can scale your dancing performance.

For example, it can be used in 'the high click':

> If you are leaning forward, tilting your head, not getting your legs up high enough, bending your knees, and missing the click, then you should scale your high click between 0–3. If your posture and carriage are perfect, but you are missing the click, you would still only give yourself an average rating between 4–7. If you have perfect posture and carriage and hit your clicks every time, then you would scale this movement between 8–10. Use this format for all of the other steps that you perform.

Having completed your scales, you will become more aware of the areas that need most attention to help improve your performance. If this is done correctly, you will discover that this simple method that I have created will work for you!

DESIGNING YOUR OWN SCALES

1. When designing your own scales, the first thing you need to do is decide on your time frame. Is it, for example, two weeks, four weeks, eight weeks and so on? Make sure that the time frame you choose is realistic. Write this time frame at the top of your chart (Figure 5.2).

FIGURE 5.2: TIME FRAME, WEEKS 1–4

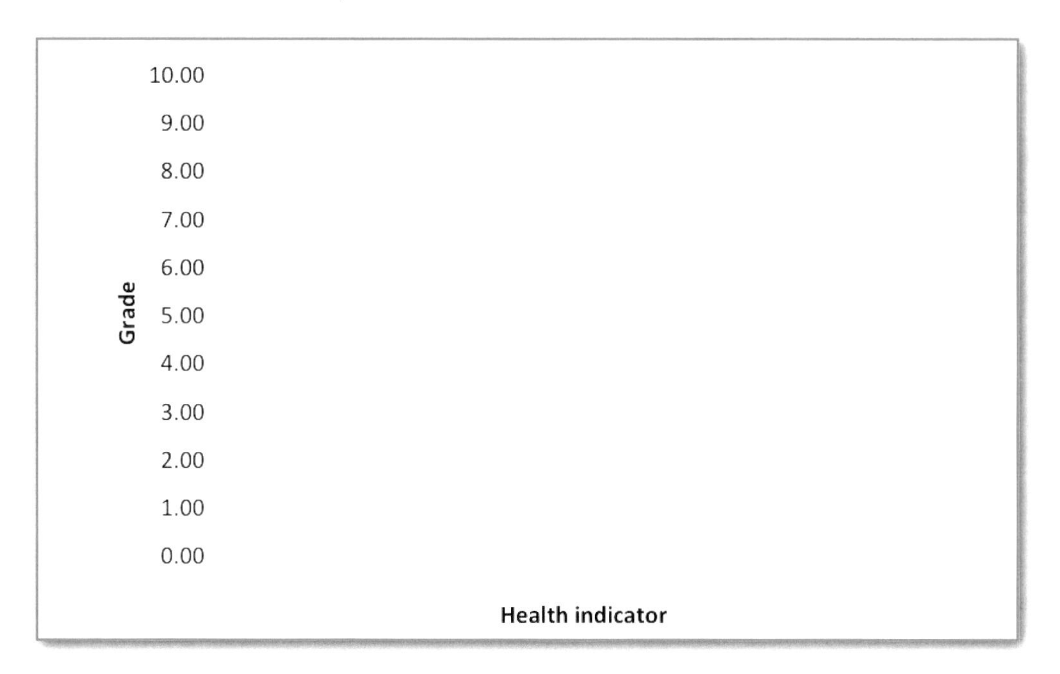

2. Choose the health indicators you want to grade, for example: body fat, blood pressure, flexibility, diet, sleep, strength levels, high clicks and overs. List these at the bottom of your chart (Figure 5.3).

FIGURE 5.3: GRADING OF HEALTH INDICATORS

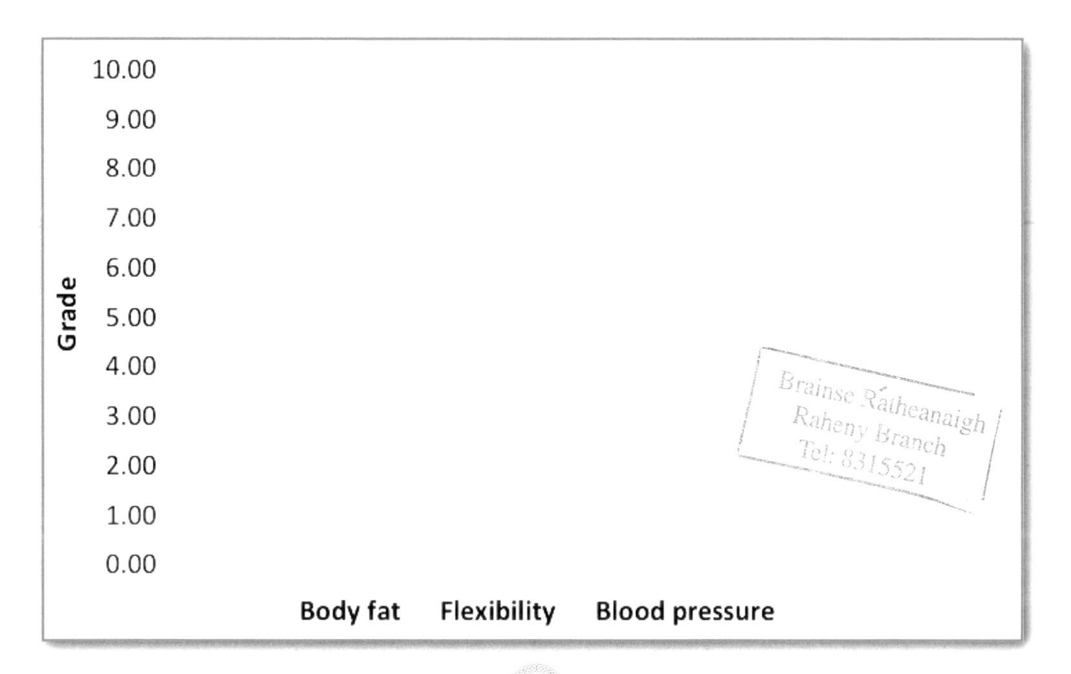

3. Decide what level you want to be at the time frame you have stated at the top of your chart. Use your 'aim' line to show this (Figure 5.4).

   For example: High Click–10, Overs–8

   Draw a 'dot' when grading each health indicator and then join the dots making an 'aim' line.

FIGURE 5.4: HEALTH AND PERFORMANCE SCALES

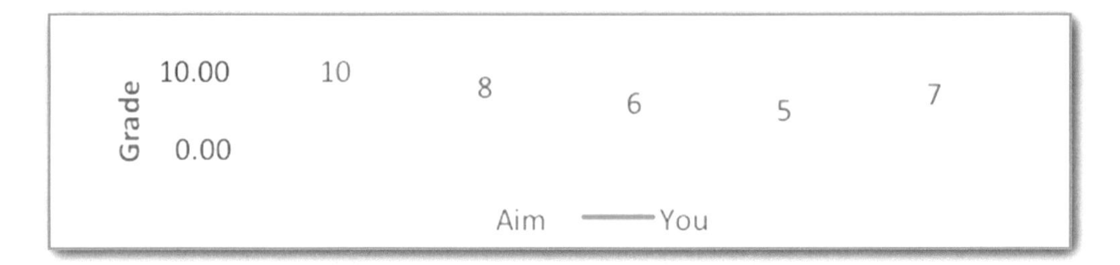

4. Choose what level you think you are now at for each health indicator, using the 'you' line. Be realistic when deciding where you think you are on the scale. Ask your teacher, parent or friend to help you if you are struggling to decide by yourself (Figure 5.5).

FIGURE 5.5: HEALTH AND PERFORMANCE SCALES

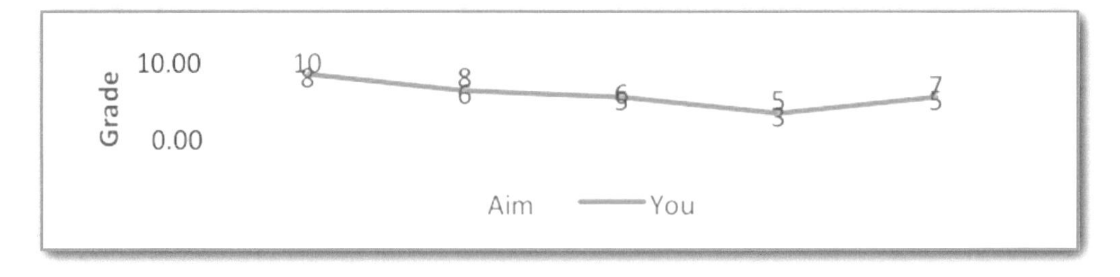

5. By now you will have chosen a time frame, the health indicators you want to grade, the level you would like to reach and the level where you think you are at present. These scales can be used to inform you of what needs most attention and what you would like to improve on most. At the end of the time frame you have set, you can look back on your chart to check if you have in fact improved on any of the health indicators you chose. Then you can start again using a new chart!

CHAPTER 6
WARM-UPS AND COOL-DOWNS

Every dance lesson should begin with a warm-up and finish with a cool-down activity. This book provides information and advice on warm-ups and cool-downs, as well as a list of related exercises that can be used to help guide you to plan your training routine.

WARM-UPS

WHAT IS A WARM-UP?

A warm-up is usually performed before participating in a sport or physical activity. It should consist of a gradual increase in intensity in physical activity, joint mobility exercises and dynamic stretching, as well as a sport-related activity.

WHY DO WE NEED TO DO WARM-UPS?

- They prepare the body and mind for the physical activity you are about to take part in.
- They increase the body's muscle temperature.
- They improve elasticity in the muscles for more strenuous activity.
- They improve joint mobility.
- They increase injury prevention.

WHAT ARE THE BENEFITS OF WARMING UP?

- It reduces muscle stiffness.
- It increases movement of blood through your tissues.
- It increases delivery of oxygen and nutrients to your muscles. This prevents you from getting out of breath early or too easily.

- It prepares your muscles for stretching.
- It prepares your heart for an increase in activity, preventing a rapid increase in blood pressure.
- It improves coordination and reaction times.

THREE STEPS TO WARMING UP

Warm-up routines involve the following three steps:

1. The general warm-up.
2. The stretching warm-up.
3. The sports-specific warm-up.

KEY POINTS

- Perform all movements slowly and within a comfortable range of motion. This will allow your muscular and nervous systems to slowly but progressively adapt to the movements.
- Warming up properly is important before performing dynamic movements, as it raises your body temperature, increases the elasticity of your muscles and prevents injury. This will also prepare you for the strenuous workout that you will perform throughout the session.
- Do not use static stretching activities before your workout. These exercises are for after your workout, during your cooling down period. This is one common mistake that all dance teachers and amateur coaches still make today.

Be sure to follow this same routine every time you are warming up.

THE GENERAL WARM-UP

The general warm-up consists of some slow to moderate intensity activities and it is performed for up to 15 minutes and no less than eight minutes, depending on the athlete and their condition.

ACTIVITIES

- A slow jog, walk or cycle
- Jump rope
- Jumping jacks
- High knees
- Body weight squats
- Body weight lunges

- Ankle bounces
- Toe walks
- Heel walks
- Spider walk

THE STRETCHING WARM-UP

Most people today still use a static stretch routine as part of their warm-up exercise. Static stretching should **never** be used after a warm-up or before your main workout. Even though your muscles and body temperature will have increased, there still is not enough elasticity in your muscles to perform a static stretch. Your next question will now be, what can I do to stretch? Dynamic stretching is the correct exercise to be used after your warm-up and before your workout. This involves joint rotations and mobility exercises. You will find these exercises in Chapter 9.

THE SPORTS-SPECIFIC WARM-UP

This is the last warming up phase and entails doing one or more exercises as part of the sport you are involved in, for example, Irish dancing.

Use simple dancing exercises during this phase. You should still avoid any sharp movements at this point, until your main workout or practice is performed.

NOTE

Please note that if you are in any pain or feeling any discomfort during the warming up phase, then you should not practice under any circumstances and you should seek advice immediately from a health professional.

Also, dance schools can have large numbers of students attending classes, which can last up to three hours. The dancers will not always be performing during this time, which means their bodies will be cooling down. When the body has cooled-down, it is not safe to dance, as this can cause injury. My advice to you is to keep moving and stay warm when you are not performing, so as to avoid injury.

COOL-DOWNS

WHAT IS A COOL-DOWN?

A cool-down is part of your daily exercise plan and involves gradually decreasing your level of activity, followed by a static stretch routine.

WHAT ARE THE BENEFITS OF A COOL-DOWN?

By gradually decreasing your level of activity, this will prepare your body to stop exercising and will prevent your muscles from getting stiff and sore. It allows the body's heart rate to steadily decrease to its normal resting rate.

COOL-DOWN EXERCISES

Most cardiovascular exercises can be used for cooling down, as long as the intensity is at a low to moderate level.

A walk or slow jog for 5–10 minutes is most commonly used, followed by a static stretch routine for 10–15 minutes. As you may be indoors and you may not have enough space, some low intensity skipping around the room is sufficient.

THE COOL-DOWN STRETCH ROUTINE

Static stretching exercises are performed after the cool-down exercise programme. These stretches are held for at least 30 seconds, to improve the range of movement and mobility. Always make sure to take your time doing these stretch exercises, as they are just as important as the rest of your workout. Dancers, in particular, need good flexibility, and the best way to increase and maintain this is by making sure you take the time at the end of each training session to perform these stretch exercises and get the best results possible. While performing all the exercises, breathe easily and never force the stretch. By this I mean any time you hold a stretch you should not feel a huge pull at the very start, but instead you should ease your way into the stretch allowing your body to complete the movement in the correct manner. You will find more details in Chapter 9.

CHAPTER 7
STRENGTH TRAINING FOR IRISH DANCERS

Before we begin discussing the exercises for strength training in depth, you will notice that most of the movements I have chosen can be performed using just your own body weight, which can be used to create an effective workout. This will enable you to exercise using the same programme in both your own home and at dance practice. Most people have become very reliant on free weights and machine weights to build strength, forgetting that they have the most effective workout tool—their own body weight! This is by far the most convenient type of resistance training. Using your own body weight, you can increase your strength, speed, power, endurance, cardiovascular levels to a degree, and even your flexibility. Taking gymnasts as an example, their natural body weight strength is truly amazing. When you watch a gymnast on the rings or on the pommel horse, he or she can manoeuvre around the apparatus with precision. In this book, I will teach you the most effective exercises to do, and I will pair them with dance steps that best relate to them.

SPINE

Your spine plays a significant role when you are dancing, creating a multidirectional movement that gives you the ability to execute dance steps with elegance and poise. For Irish dancing, your spine must portray a rigid, stable and elegant appearance. It must be strong to perform this activity. This strength depends on the balance and organisation of the muscle contractions. You must have a healthy balance of muscle action, which will then support the proper alignment of your spine. Irish dancing can place a great deal of stress on the spine, and learning to support it by performing the following exercises will help you to improve your stability and can reduce the risk of injury:

DEAD BUGS

PURPOSE

Irish dancing requires a large amount of trunk control in a neutral position in order to maintain stability throughout a performance. This exercise will teach you how to control your pelvis and spine, whilst moving your legs. You must remember that only your legs do the work, not your pelvis or spine.

MUSCLES USED

Transverse abdominis, external obliques and multifidi.

EXECUTION

Lie on your back, with your arms by your side at a 45º angle. Engage your abdominals, making sure that your back is flat against the floor. Lift both legs to a 90º hip flexion position, and also a 90º knee flexion position. Make sure your hips are in line with your knees.

Engage your abdominals. Let one leg glide away from you to allow your knee to fully extend. Focus on keeping your transverse abdominis and external obliques engaged, to ensure pelvic stabilisation.

Bring your leg back to the starting position. Repeat the sequence with the other leg.

Do 12 repetitions.

Complete three sets.

NOTE

It is important to maintain stability in your lower back. If your back starts to overextend when straightening your leg, do not lower your leg too near to the ground. Only lower your leg when your back is stable.

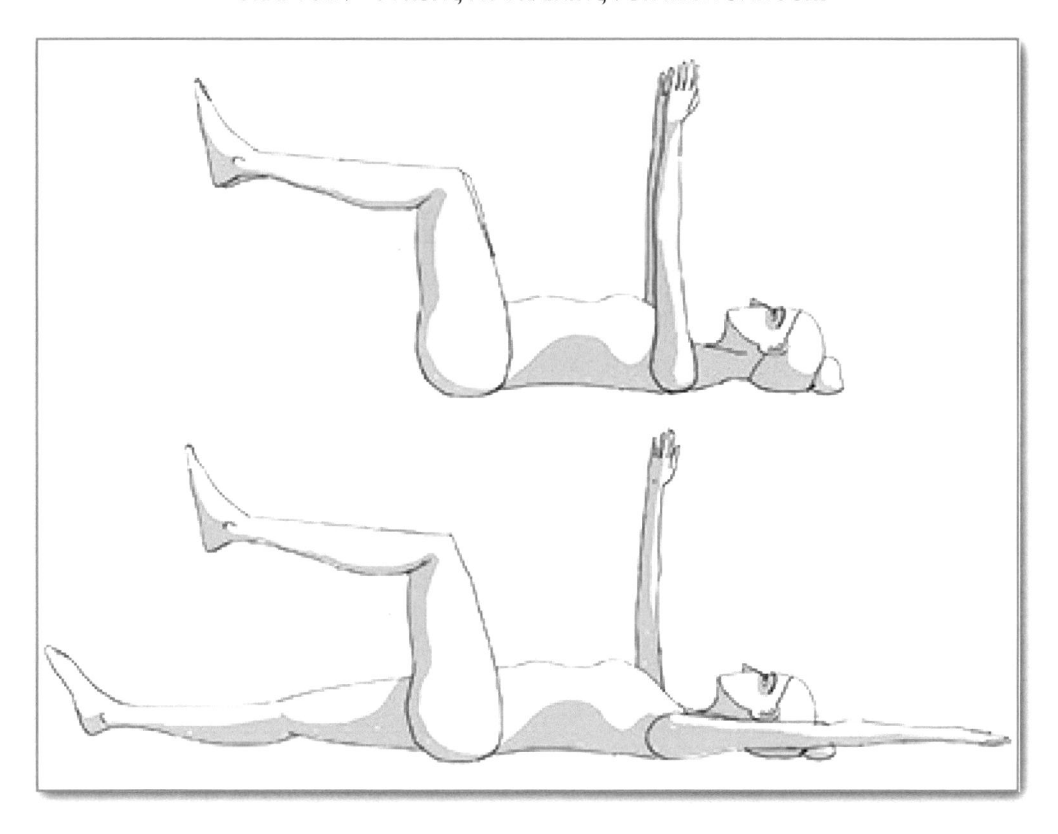

FIGURE 7.1: DEADBUGS – MUSCLES USED: TRANSVERSE ABDOMINIS, EXTERNAL OBLIQUES AND MULTIFIDI

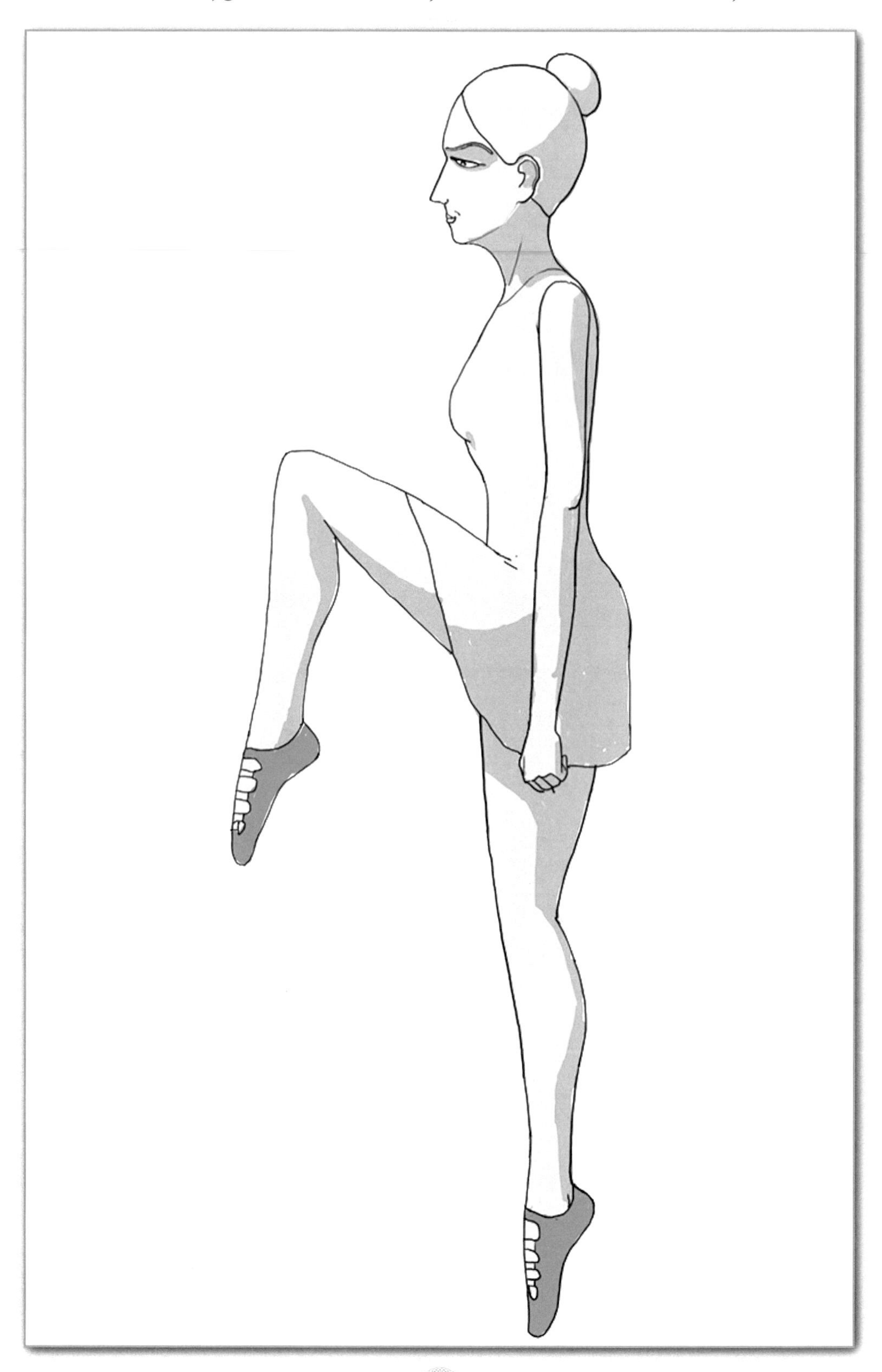

HIP FLEXOR ISOMETRICS

PURPOSE

This exercise will help you to locate the iliopsoas muscle. This muscle will assist you to lift your legs higher than 90º. Never allow this muscle to shorten. If it does, it can pull your lower back into an arched position, resulting in poor posture when lifting your legs higher than 90º.

MUSCLES USED

Iliopsoas.

EXECUTION

Lie on your back. Bend both knees, with feet flat on the ground. Engage the abdominals, ensuring that your back is also flat against the ground. Do this for the remainder of the exercise.

Elevate your leg, keeping the knee bent and also turning it outwards.

Press the hand closest to you against your leg, so as to perform an isometric contraction of the iliopsoas (this is what you would do if someone were to hit you in the stomach). Hold for five seconds and then relax.

Do 12 repetitions.

Complete three sets.

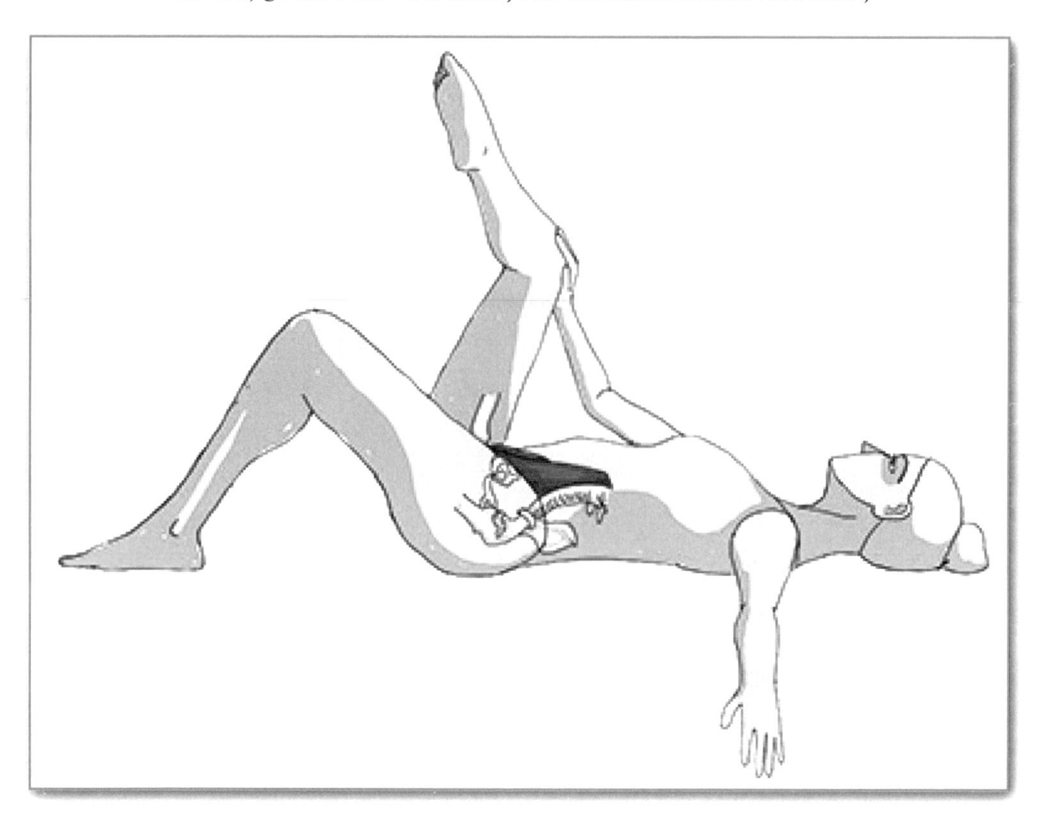

FIGURE 7.2: HIP FLEXOR ISOMETRICS – MUSCLES USED: ILIOPSOAS

SPINAL BRACE

PURPOSE

Irish dancing can place a great deal of pressure on the spine. This simple exercise will help you to build strength around the spinal area, to secure and brace it. All movements required of you when dancing should be initiated by the contraction of the multifidi muscles and the abdominals.

MUSCLES USED

Multifidi.

EXECUTION

Lie on your front, with a pillow placed at your waist for support. Then put your hands in front of your forehead.

Lift your head and shoulders slowly and in a controlled manner, keeping your hands in front of your forehead. Isometrically contract your abdominals and the muscles along your spine.

When you have reached a maximum elevation, with your spine in a slightly long, arched position, hold for up to five seconds. Slowly return to the starting position.

Do 12 repetitions.

Complete three sets.

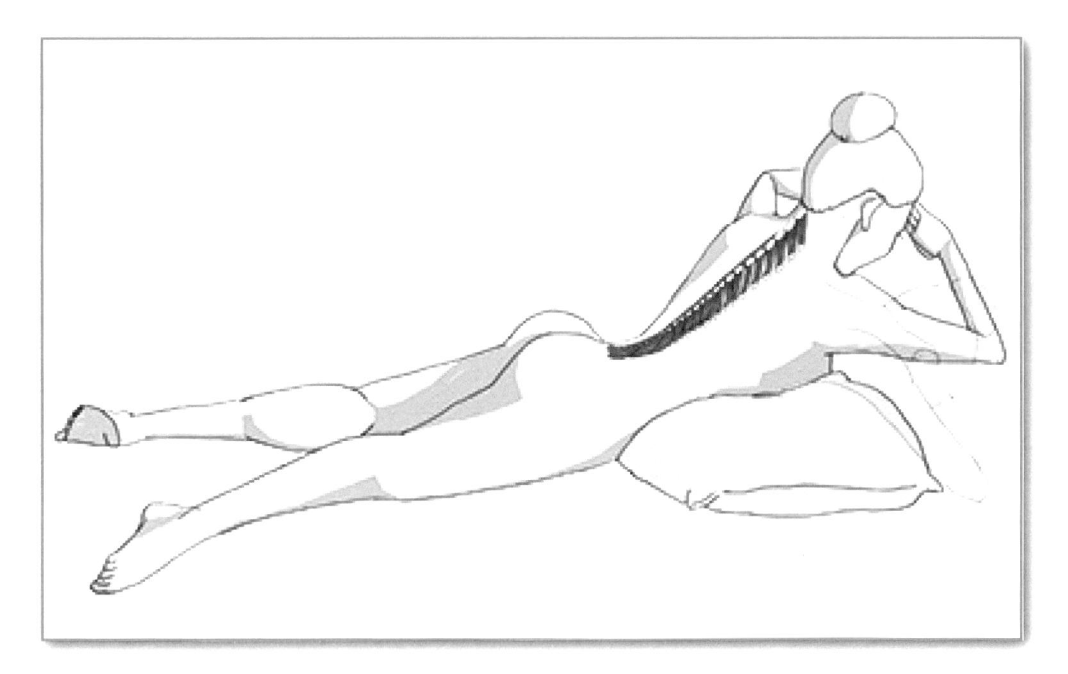

FIGURE 7.3: SPINAL BRACE – MUSCLES USED: MULTIFIDI

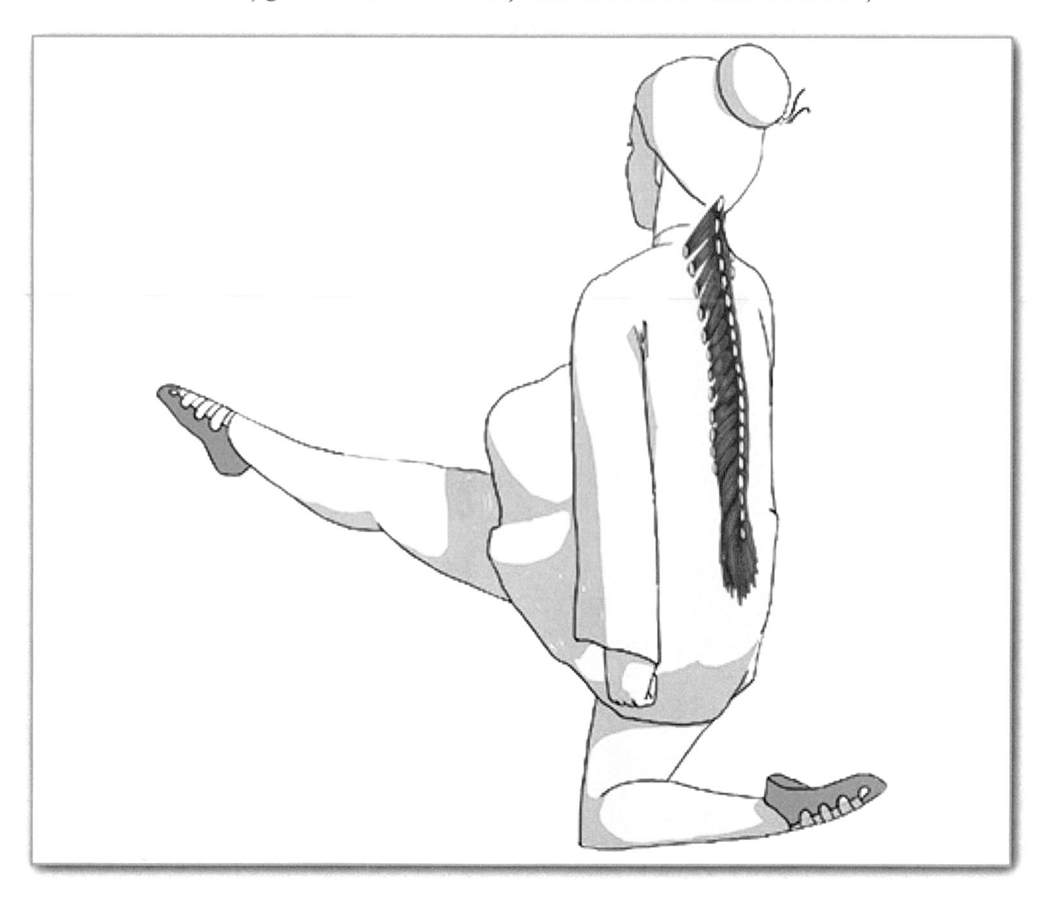

ISCHIAL SQUEEZE

PURPOSE

Your pelvic floor muscles provide a base for your pelvis. This exercise helps to strengthen the pelvic floor. Performing this exercise not only helps to improve your bladder and bowel control, but also your fine movements, leading to large improvements in body support.

MUSCLES USED

Pelvic floor muscles.

EXECUTION

Sit on a stool or a chair. Turn your hips and legs slightly outward. Locate your neutral alignment. Make sure you are not rounding your shoulders, resulting in an arched back, and that you are not overextending your back. Rest with your arms in a crossed position, in front of your chest.

Engage your pelvic floor muscles and visualise these muscles shortening, allowing your pubic and coccyx bones to pull closer together. Then relax and notice how they eccentrically lengthen (stretch in response to a greater opposing force).

Repeat this exercise until you get familiar with the muscles that are working and how they relate to the sit bones. Notice how your spine lifts as you contract.

Do 12 repetitions.

Complete three sets.

FIGURE 7.4: ISCHIAL SQUEEZE – MUSCLES USED: PELVIC FLOOR MUSCLES

CORE

Where is your core? If you ask people this question most of them will point to their abdominals. If you ask a professional trainer, some will tell you that your core is between your chest and your pelvis, more might say it is between your knees and shoulders, while others might claim it is between your shoulders and your pelvis. While you may get different definitions, a simple answer is that the core is your body minus your arms and legs.

YOUR CORE IS YOUR FOUNDATION.

All movements used in Irish dancing are highly dependent on the core. It is your foundation. To enable you to dance using challenging movements with ease, you need to have a strong foundation which will create good spinal stability and postural awareness. One of your first steps as an Irish dancer was to learn how to do 'a lift (a movement where both feet are off the floor) or an over (as some dancers may call it)'.

FIGURE 7.5: CORE

To create this movement it requires core strength. When you lift or jump you must use your core to brace the spine for protection, to prevent it from collapsing. Again, putting it in simple terms, a strong core foundation allows for more control of your movements.

SIDE BEND

PURPOSE

It is very easy to allow the body to lean to one side when in a standing position, because gravity will help you to do so, especially if you have good flexibility. As this creates a negative appearance when dancing, we must learn to prevent the body from doing this. The side bend exercise provides the support you need to control the movement and prevent it from occurring. If gravity can pull you into a side bend, then your muscles are not strong enough, and you will have to work harder to stay in the correct upright position. After performing this exercise, you will have more control and you will not even have to think about standing in an upright position.

MUSCLES USED

Rectus abdominus, external and internal obliques and quadratus lumborum.

EXECUTION

Lie on the floor. Bend your knees, keeping your feet flat on the floor and hip-width apart. Engage your abdominal muscles to help raise your trunk slightly.

Exhale. Keeping your hands close to your side, begin to move to your left, bringing your left hand closer to your left heel. Your trunk should be slightly above the floor. Move as far as you can without overstretching your right hip.

Inhale. Return to your centre in a controlled manner.

Repeat on the other side.

Do 12 repetitions on each side.

Complete three sets.

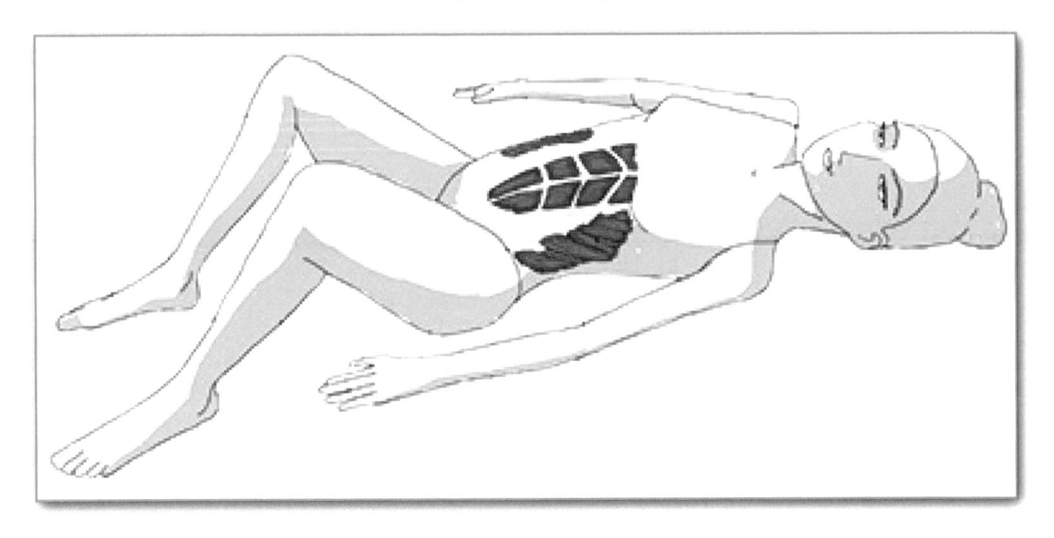

FIGURE 7.6: SIDE BEND – MUSCLES USED: RECTUS ABDOMINUS, EXTERNAL AND INTERNAL OBLIQUES AND QUADRATUS LUMBORUM

SIT-UPS

PURPOSE

When done correctly, sit-ups are a safe and effective abdominal exercise. The characteristics of effective exercises are that the movement allows you to bend the spine in its full range of motion, while contracting the abdominals from full extension to full flexion. Turn your knees out, while placing them in a bent position. This will take the hip flexors out of the equation, allowing you to focus more on the abdominals, when completing the movement. Strength in the rectus abdominus will provide power for the trunk. The stronger these muscles are, the more powerful this portion of your trunk will be.

MUSCLES USED

Rectus abdominus and the anterior fibres of the external obliques.

EXECUTION

Sit on the floor, with your knees bent and the soles of your feet together. Start by sitting in an upright position, keeping your head, shoulders and hips aligned. Engage your abdominals at all times during this exercise. Place an AbMat (abdominal training gym mat) or a rolled-up towel under the lumbar curve. This allows the abdominal muscles to contract from full extension to full flexion.

Inhale. Lie onto your back slowly in a controlled manner, keeping your arms straight at all times, until your shoulder blades and your hands are touching the ground. Do not allow gravity to drop you to the floor too quickly.

Exhale. Contract your rectus abdominus muscles to lift your trunk off the floor. Return to the starting position by sitting up at a controlled tempo. Keep your body upright, head and shoulders in a neutral position and your arms straight, bringing them down in front of you to touch your toes.

Do 12 repetitions.

Complete three sets.

As you become stronger increase the repetitions and sets.

NOTE

Avoid lifting and pulling yourself up from the lying position with your head, neck and hip flexors. This can result in neck pain, headaches and lower back injuries. Do not increase repetitions unless you are able to maintain control and alignment.

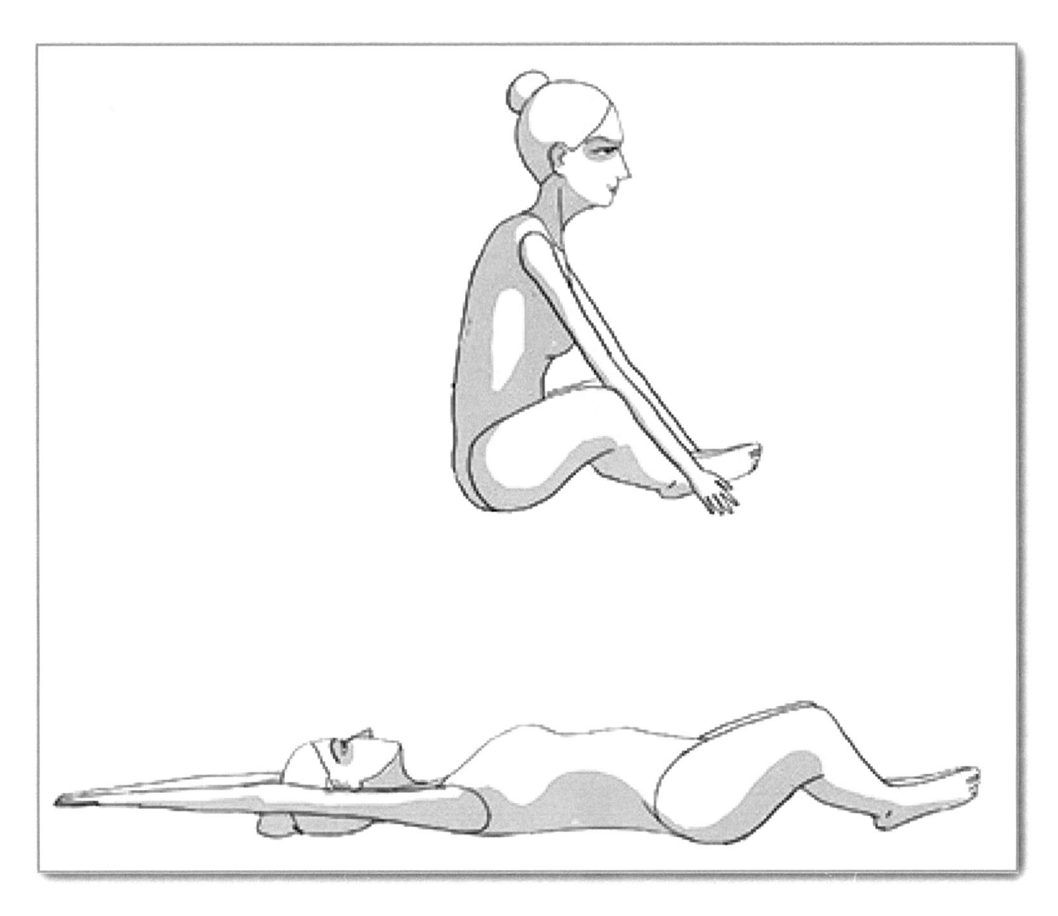

FIGURE 7.7: SIT-UPS – MUSCLES USED: RECTUS ABDOMINUS AND THE ANTERIOR FIBRES OF THE EXTERNAL OBLIQUES

COCCYX BALANCE

PURPOSE

When performing steps that require you to defy gravity such as 'a lift', your legs can feel very heavy and you end up struggling to execute the movement. The resistance that your legs provide can pull on your lower spine, resulting in poor quality dancing and it also increases the risk of injury. A good balance between abdominal control and hip flexor strength will prevent this from happening.

MUSCLES USED

Transverse abdominus, rectus abdominus, external oblique, internal oblique and iliopsoas.

EXECUTION

Lie on the floor. Bend your knees, keeping your feet flat on the ground and also hip-width apart. Place your arms by your side, keeping them straight and your thumbs pointing upward.

Exhale. Lift your trunk and your knees, while raising your arms at the same time. Balance the movement with your hip flexors, as well as your abdominals, and then find your centre. Hold the position for up to 10 seconds.

Inhale. Return to the starting position in a controlled manner. When you are doing this, be sure that you are still using the hip flexor action and the abdominal contraction.

Do 12 repetitions.

Complete three sets.

NOTE

If you cannot complete this exercise without causing your lower back to fall into an extension, then do not attempt this exercise.

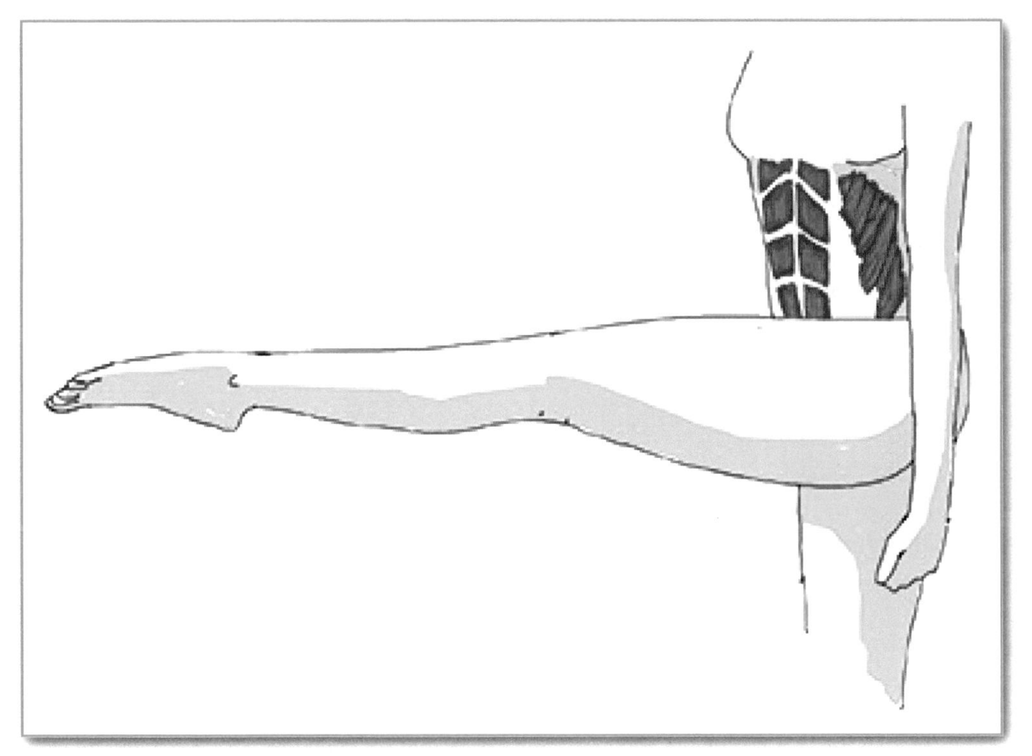

FIGURE 7.8: COCCYX BALANCE – MUSCLES USED: TRANSVERSE ABDOMINUS, RECTUS ABDOMINUS, EXTERNAL OBLIQUE, INTERNAL OBLIQUE AND ILIOPSOAS

BACK EXTENSION

PURPOSE

A dancer is expected to keep his or her spine straight and strong when performing. However, they tend to extend the spine when their body tires, or when complicated movements have to be performed. The back extension exercise will help you to strengthen the muscles used when the spine extends, to avoid injury. The abdominal exercises will help to brace and support your spine along the front of your body.

MUSCLES USED

Pelvic floor muscles, multifidi, quadratus lumborum, internal oblique, external oblique and erector spinae.

EXECUTION

Lie face down on the floor. Rest your arms by your side, with your thumbs pointing downward. Fully extend your legs, with your feet turned out slightly and hip-width apart. Squeeze your gluteals and sit bones, while lengthening your spine.

Inhale first and then exhale, as you lift your upper body, whilst keeping your hands by your side and your feet on the ground. Feel the extension through your spine, and also notice your gluteals working harder. Try to lift your sternum off the floor. Hold for three seconds.

Inhale. Return to the starting position in a controlled manner.

Do 12 repetitions.

Complete three sets.

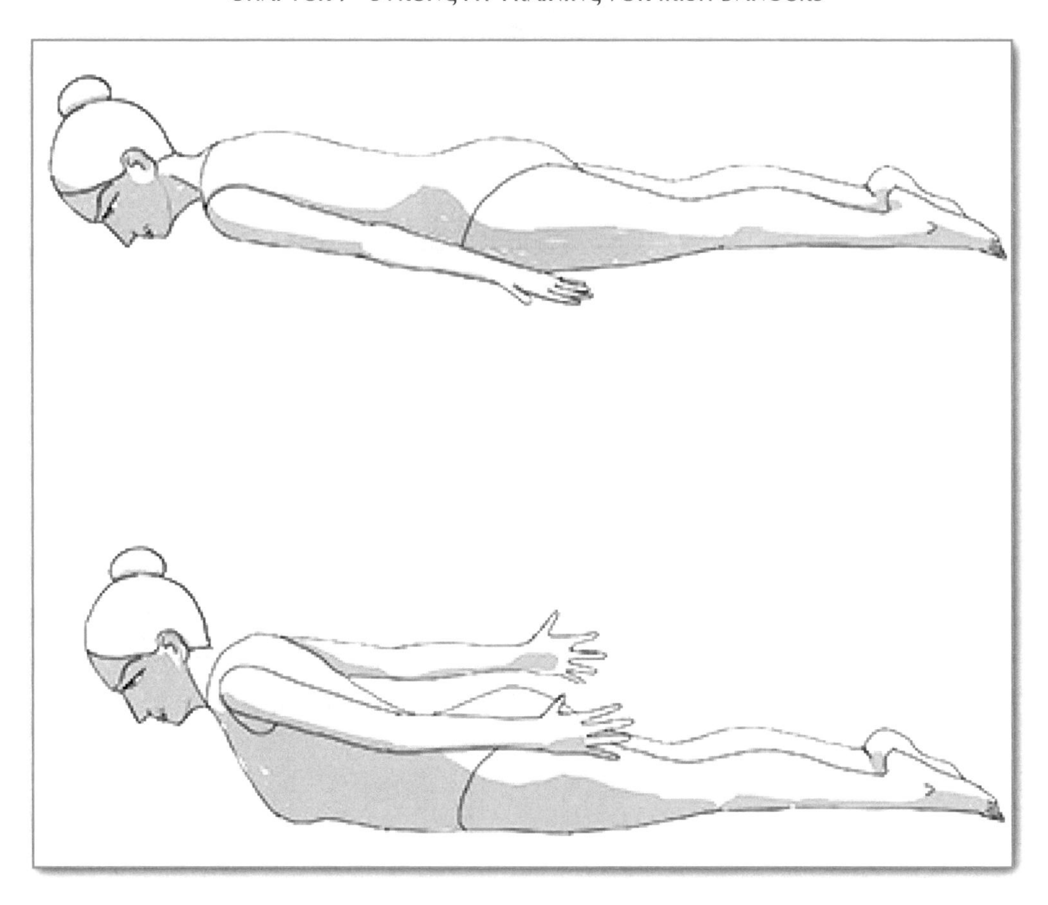

FIGURE 7.9: BACK EXTENSION – MUSCLES USED: PELVIC FLOOR MUSCLES, MULTIFIDI, QUADRATUS LUMBORUM, INTERNAL OBLIQUE, EXTERNAL OBLIQUE AND ERECTOR SPINAE

ROWING WITH A RESISTANCE BAND

PURPOSE

It is normal practice in Irish dancing to push your shoulders back. As the shoulder blades move back and into retraction, the chest and ribcage open, resulting in an abnormal posture. When you are in this position, your core needs to work harder. To prevent the chest from expanding, you must strengthen the trapezius, rhomboids and levator scapulae muscles. These muscles will improve your posture and the position of your shoulders. When you have a strong awareness of your ability to keep your shoulders back, using little effort during this exercise, you can then increase the resistance of the band to make the workout more effective.

MUSCLES USED

Trapezius, rhomboid and levator scapulae.

EXECUTION

Sit on the floor, keeping your legs straight and your trunk in a neutral position. Secure a resistance band around the soles of both feet. Cross over the band and hold both ends in your hands. Keep your elbows tight against your torso.

Inhale. On exhalation, pull the resistance band towards you, keeping your elbows tight against your torso. Feel your scapula pulling together. Engage your abdominals throughout the movement, to maintain a firm centre and to avoid overextending your back.

Hold for three seconds. Return to the starting position slowly and in a controlled manner. Avoid rounding your shoulders inwards towards your chest.

Do 12 repetitions.

Complete three sets.

NOTE

You can perform this exercise while keeping your elbows slightly below shoulder height. However, it is better that Irish dancers hold their elbows tightly against their torso.

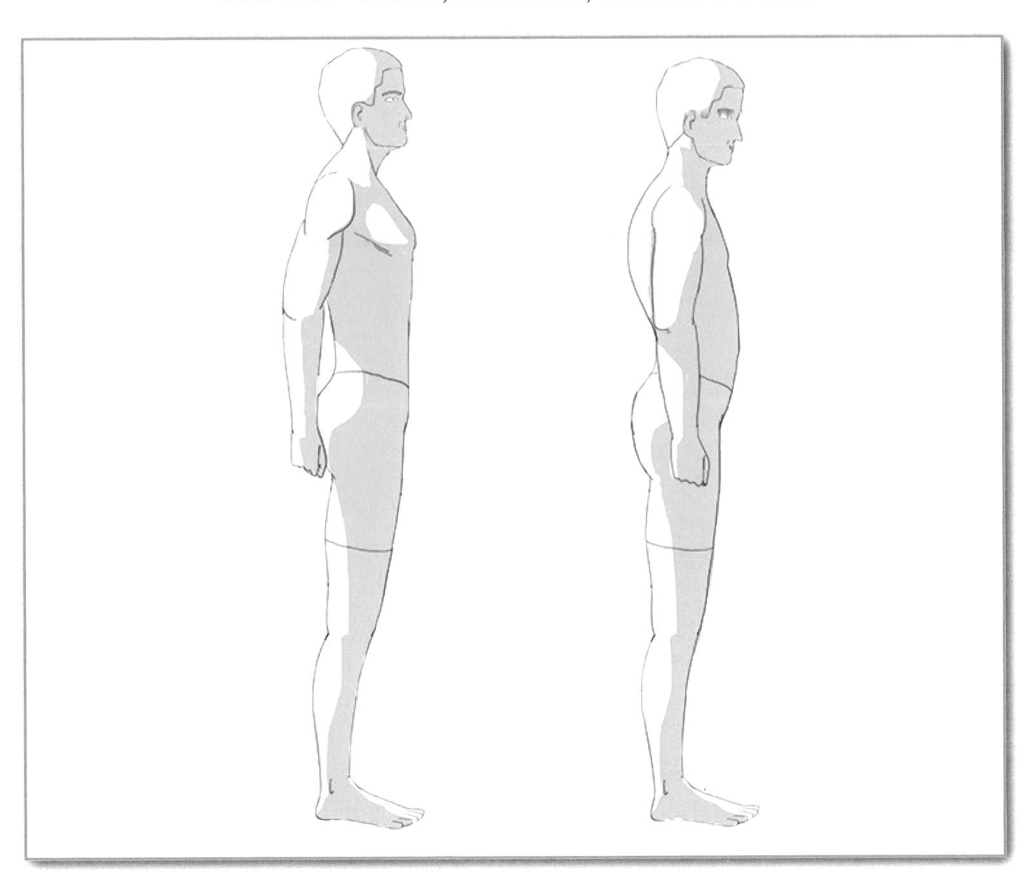

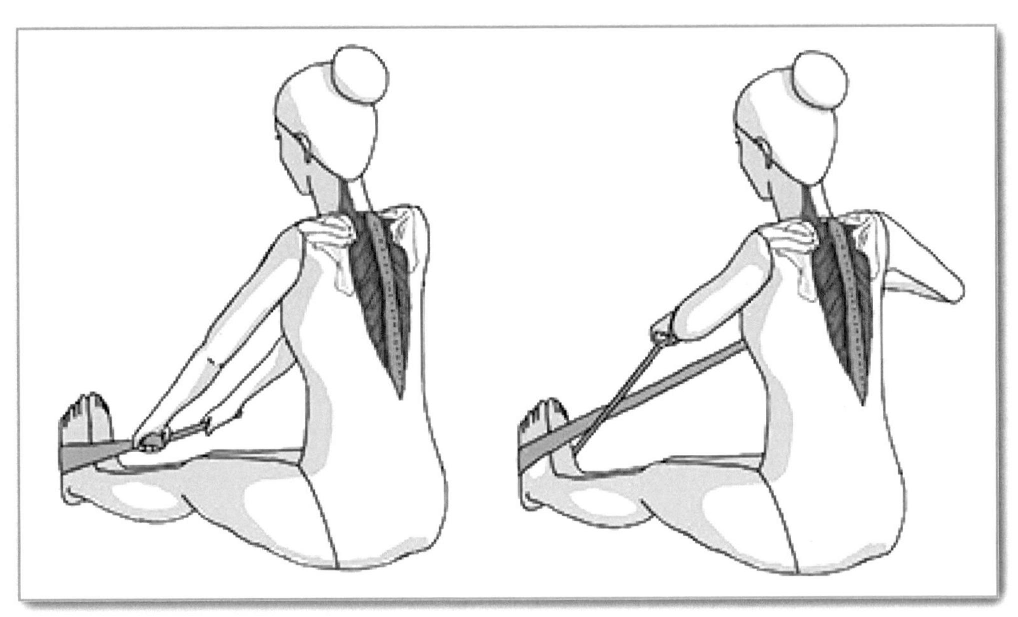

FIGURE 7.10: ROWING WITH A RESISTANCE BAND – MUSCLES USED: TRAPEZIUS, RHOMBOID AND LEVATOR SCAPULAE

PUSH-UPS

PURPOSE

Push–up exercises not only build upper body strength and power, but they also focus on the core and gluteal muscle groups. One of the most common reasons for poor posture is a lack of core strength. In order for you to hold your shoulders back when dancing, your core must be properly activated and strong enough to support a vertical stance. Performing push-ups regularly will result in better posture, over the course of time.

MUSCLES USED

Pectoralis major, triceps brachii, anterior deltoid, serratus anterior, trapezius and rectus abdominus.

EXECUTION

Place your hands wider than shoulder-width apart and your feet hip-width apart. (If you are resting on your knees, make sure you keep your feet off the ground). Check that your body is in a straight line, from your heels to your head, and that your hands are placed directly under your elbows.

Engage your gluteals and abdominals. Lower your body until your chest touches the ground. Keep your hips and shoulders in line at all times.

Raise your body to the starting position, until your elbows are fully extended.

NOTE

Throughout the exercise, avoid overextending your lower back, by sagging your hips towards the ground.

FIGURE 7.11: PUSH-UPS – MUSCLES USED: PECTORALIS MAJOR, TRICEPS BRACHII, ANTERIOR DELTOID, SERRATUS ANTERIOR, TRAPEZIUS AND RECTUS ABDOMINUS

FIGURE 7.11: PUSH-UPS – MUSCLES USED: PECTORALIS MAJOR, TRICEPS BRACHII, ANTERIOR DELTOID, SERRATUS ANTERIOR, TRAPEZIUS AND RECTUS ABDOMINUS

PELVIS AND HIPS

Irish dancing puts extreme pressure on the hip joints, as it requires unusual repetitive movements which demand extreme control. This section will focus on how to enhance the function and strength of the pelvis and hip joints, which will improve a dancer's technique and reduce faulty movements. Strengthening the pelvis and hips will minimise the risk of injury such as lower back, hip, knee and ankle problems. If these injuries do not suddenly occur, then 9 times out of 10 they are related to faulty techniques due to poor body alignment in the lower spine and pelvis. When I assess my dancing client's body alignment, I usually see that improvement is needed. As the body works as a whole, when there is poor pelvis and hip alignment, this can result in using other muscles and joints in an abnormal fashion to complete the movement. When performing the exercises in this section, make sure that you work the body as a whole, maintaining an even weight throughout and keeping your hips in line.

GLUTE BRIDGE

PURPOSE

The main aim when performing a glute bridge exercise is to lift the hips with your glute muscles. Try to avoid using your hamstrings and spinal erectors. Many people initially feel their hamstrings working when performing this exercise instead of the gluteus maximus. If this happens, bend your knees further to shorten the hamstring muscle, reducing its contribution to the movement. The glute bridge activates the glutes to improve hip stabilisation and prevents the back from extending, which is ideal for Irish dancing.

MUSCLES USED

Gluteus maximus, gluteus minimus, gluteus medius, hamstrings and adductors.

EXECUTION

Lie on your back. Bend your knees to a 90° angle and keep the soles of your feet flat on the ground. Keep your arms by your side at 45°, with your palms facing down.

Exhale. Lift your hips, keeping all the weight on your heels and your shoulder blades. Move through the hips until your body is straight from your knees to your shoulder blades.

Inhale. Hold the bridge position for three seconds and then lower your hips slowly and in a controlled manner back to the starting position.

NOTE

A more advanced form of this exercise is the single leg glute bridge. Both exercises have the same position and movement, however with the single leg glute bridge only one leg is fixed to the ground and the other leg is raised off the floor, ideally at a 90° angle. The leg you raise must remain straight throughout the movement.

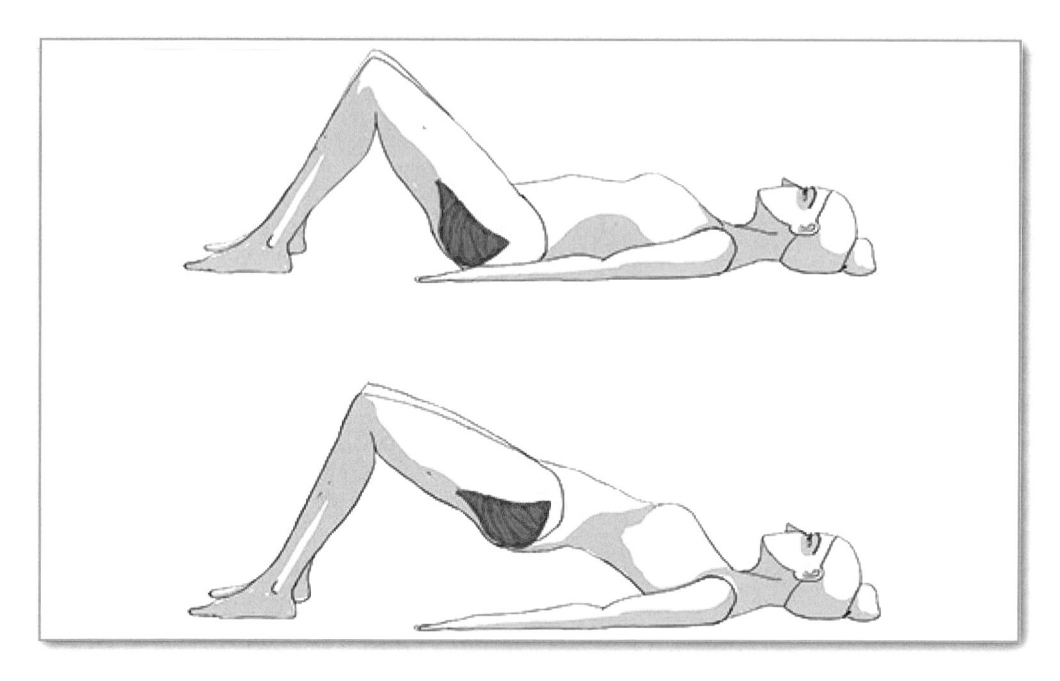

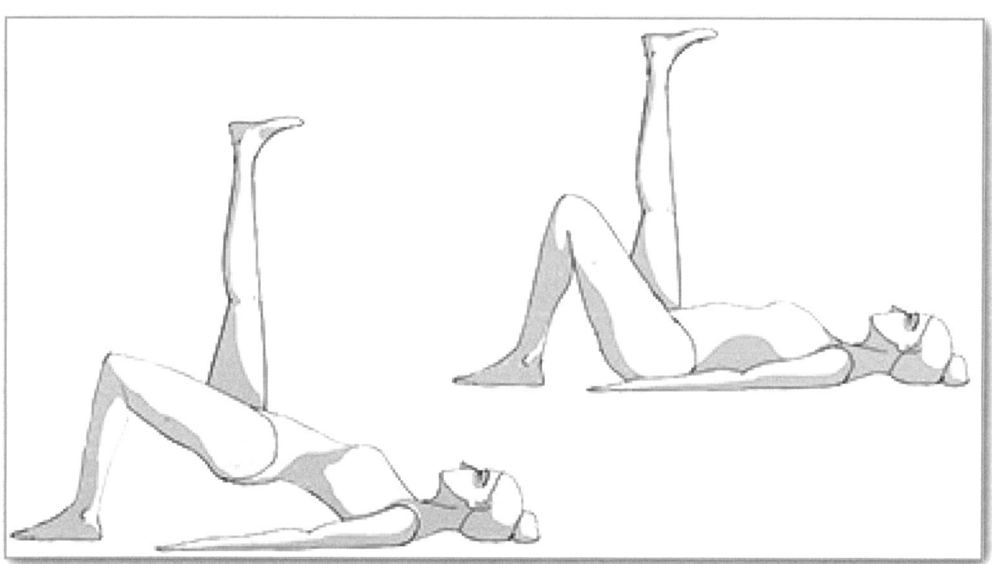

FIGURE 7.12: GLUTE BRIDGE – MUSCLES USED: GLUTEUS MAXIMUS, GLUTEUS MINIMUS, GLUTEUS MEDIUS, HAMSTRINGS AND ADDUCTORS

LATERAL BAND WALK

PURPOSE

This exercise, when done correctly, is the best way to improve hip and knee joint stability, as well as strengthening the hip abductors. It should be included as part of your warm-up routine, to prepare the body for dance techniques that involve impact on the hip and knee joints, such as jumping.

MUSCLES USED

Abductors, abdominals and gluteus medius.

EXECUTION

Position a resistance band around your lower legs. Placing the band close to your knees will make this exercise easier, while putting it closer to your ankles will create a more advanced form of this exercise.

With the band in place, stand with your feet shoulder-width apart and your knees and hips slightly bent. Keeping your trunk in an upright position, with your head held up, look straight ahead.

Staying in a low position throughout the movement, take a slow and controlled lateral step. After taking the step, bring your feet close together again, using your opposite leg. Keep your feet at least shoulder-width apart, to feel tension from the resistance band. Make sure your toes are always pointing forward.

Continue to laterally step to one side until you have completed up to 20 steps.

Then complete 20 lateral steps in the opposite direction.

Complete three sets.

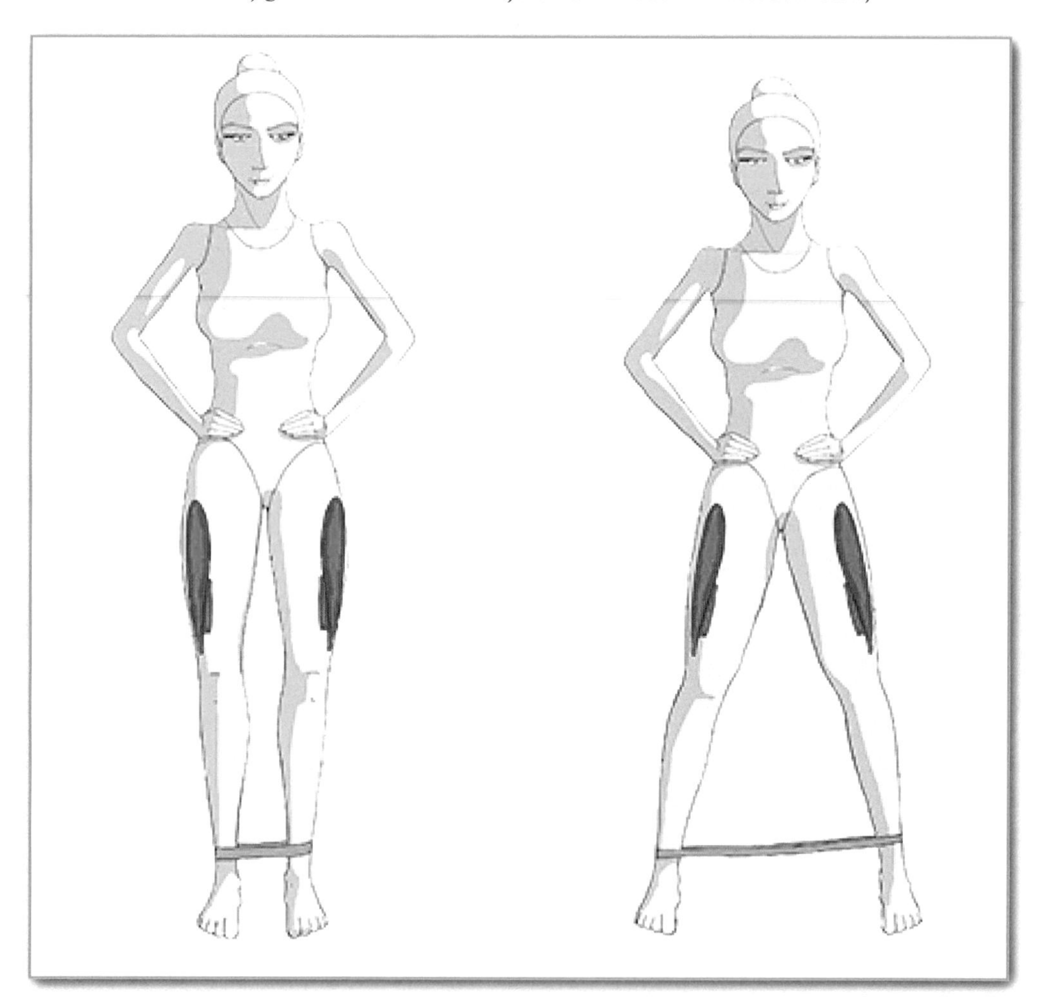

FIGURE 7.13: LATERAL BAND WALKS

SIDE PLANK

PURPOSE

This is a very important exercise, as it creates a strong core foundation. This exercise helps you to gain strength, which enables you to maintain security in your centre, when performing steps that require a steady and powerful appearance.

MUSCLES USED

Transverse abdominus, external oblique, internal oblique, quadratus lumborum, erector spinae and multifidi.

EXECUTION

Lie on your right side, with your legs extended and one foot on top of the other. Support your upper body with your right elbow and forearm. Place your elbow under your shoulder. Rest your left arm on your side.

Inhale and then exhale. As you exhale, lift your hips off the ground and activate your trunk muscles. Focus on your centre and your balance. Maintain this position for up to 12 seconds and then repeat on the other side.

Hold for 12 seconds on each side.

Complete three sets.

NOTE

Avoid putting all the weight on your shoulder, which could cause pain and discomfort. Keep your trunk raised and avoid lowering your hips as you tire. When this happens, it is best to simply rest.

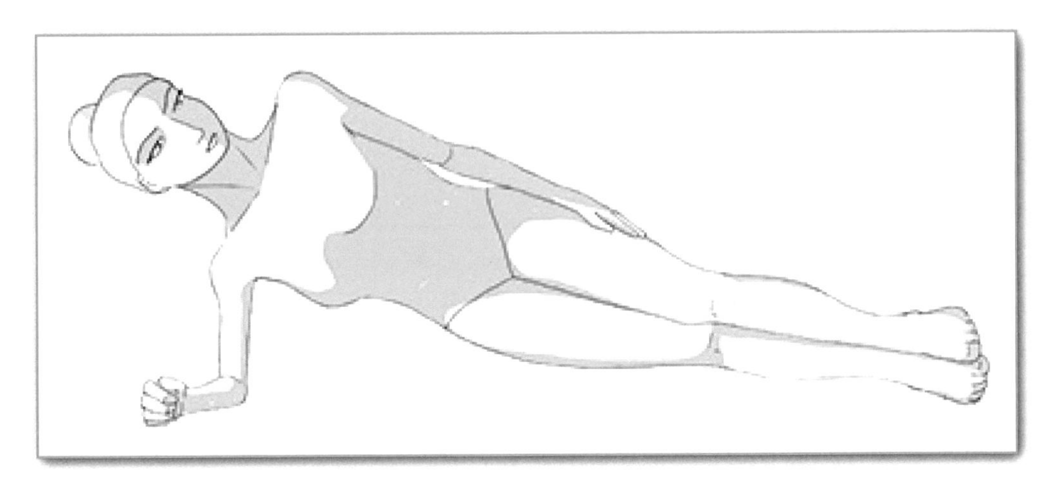

FIGURE 7.14: SIDE PLANK – MUSCLES USED: TRANSVERSE ABDOMINUS, EXTERNAL OBLIQUE, INTERNAL OBLIQUE, QUADRATUS LUMBORUM, ERECTOR SPINAE AND MULTIFIDI

LEGS

The beauty of Irish dancing comes from the steps you create with your legs and feet. This is what attracts an audience— the judges, your teachers, your family and your friends. Obviously, you must learn to control the whole body when dancing, but in this section we will focus on the legs, to create precision in your movements. Each of the following exercises relate to your dancing techniques. Try to visualise these techniques and figure out where they are put into practice in your steps.

SHORT ARCS

PURPOSE

You must respond quickly in the take-off phase of a jump or a lift, and then slow down when landing. This exercise creates strength in the quadriceps to enable you to do this.

MUSCLES USED

Rectus femoris, vastus lateralis, vastus medialis, adductor longus, adductor brevis, adductor magnus, gracilis and pectineus.

EXECUTION

While lying on your back, put a foam roller that is longer than the width of your hips under your knees. Also place a small ball between your knees.

Your feet should be flat in the starting position. Make sure that your body is in a neutral position and engage the core before you perform each repetition.

Lift both legs simultaneously, tightening the quadriceps, and squeezing the ball to activate the adductors.

Extend both knees and hold for three seconds before returning in a controlled manner.

Do 12 repetitions.

Complete three sets.

NOTE

Do not rotate the knee or foot while performing this exercise.

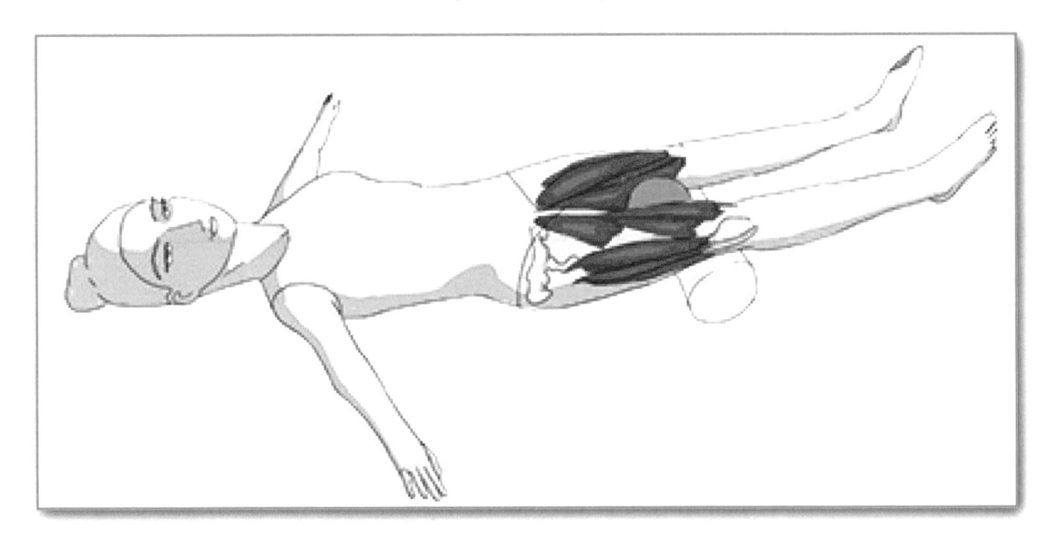

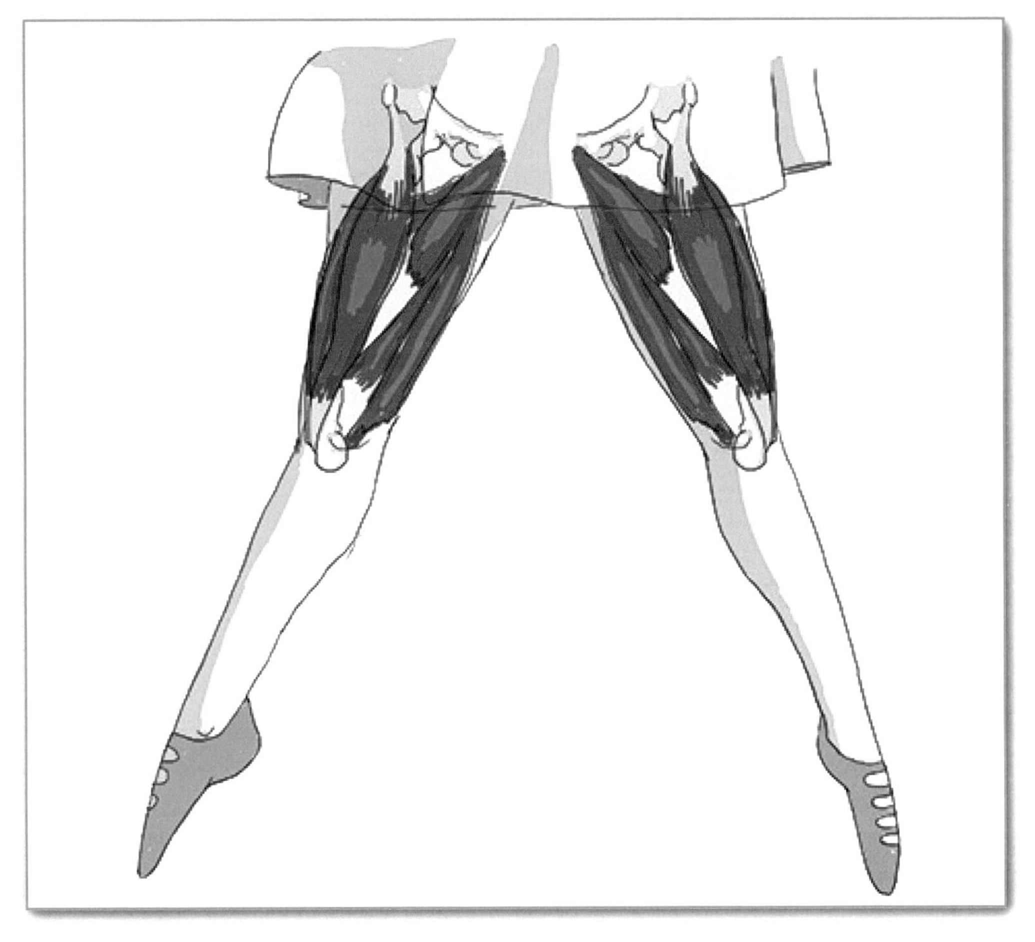

FIGURE 7.15: SHORT ARCS – MUSCLES USED: RECTUS FEMORIS, VASTUS LATERALIS, VASTUS MEDIALIS, ADDUCTOR LONGUS, ADDUCTOR BREVIS, ADDUCTOR MAGNUS, GRACILIS AND PECTINEUS

AIR SQUAT

PURPOSE

When performed correctly and safely, squats will help you to move faster on stage, jump higher, increase your mobility, decrease joint pain and reduce the risk of injury. They require you to use the same muscles as you use when dancing, which indicates straight away that squats are very important and should always be part of a training routine. Bend your knees during any dance movement relating to the squat.

Eventually, squatting using just your own body weight will become too easy and you will have to include weights. If you do not have the equipment for this, or you do not feel comfortable using weights, you can always advance to single leg squats or other variations on body weight squats.

When advancing from an air squat, my next recommendation would be to progress to a Bulgarian split squat.

MUSCLES USED

Gluteus medius, gluteus maximus, vastus lateralis, rectus femoris, vastus intermedius and vastus medialis.

EXECUTION

Stand with your heels at shoulder-width apart. Put most of your weight on your heels. Make sure your hips and knees are fully extended. Keep your chest up and engage your abdominals to ensure a neutral spine. Keep your arms straight and in front of your chest throughout the movement.

Inhale. Bend your knees, keeping them behind your toes at all times. Squat until the hip crease is below the top of your kneecap (parallel). Keep your knees in line with your feet and your head in a neutral position.

Exhale. Return in a controlled manner to full extension of the hips and knees.

Do 12 repetitions.

Complete three sets.

FIGURE 7.16: AIR SQUAT – MUSCLES USED: GLUTEUS MEDIUS, GLUTEUS MAXIMUS, VASTUS LATERALIS, RECTUS FEMORIS, VASTUS INTERMEDIUS AND VASTUS MEDIALIS

HAMSTRING CURL

PURPOSE

The main purpose of the hamstrings is to flex the knee and extend the hip. They perform for you each time you bend your knee and bring your heels towards your gluteals. The bicep femoris also assists your turnouts and you will feel it contract as you point your toe and turn out your foot. However, this is not the only exercise you must work on to perfect your turnouts.

MUSCLES USED

Biceps femoris, semitendinosus, semimembranosus and gluteus maximus.

EXECUTION

Lie down on your front. Rest your forehead on your hands. Put your legs together and in a parallel position. Bend your knees to a 90° angle and flex your ankles. Your knees and ankles must be touching,

Engage your abdominals and lift both thighs about an inch (2.5 cm) off the ground. Engage your hamstrings and gluteals and hold for five seconds.

Do 12 repetitions.

Complete three sets.

NOTE

Avoid arching your lower spine, by engaging the abdominals and the muscles along the lower spine. Your body must stay in a neutral position when performing this exercise.

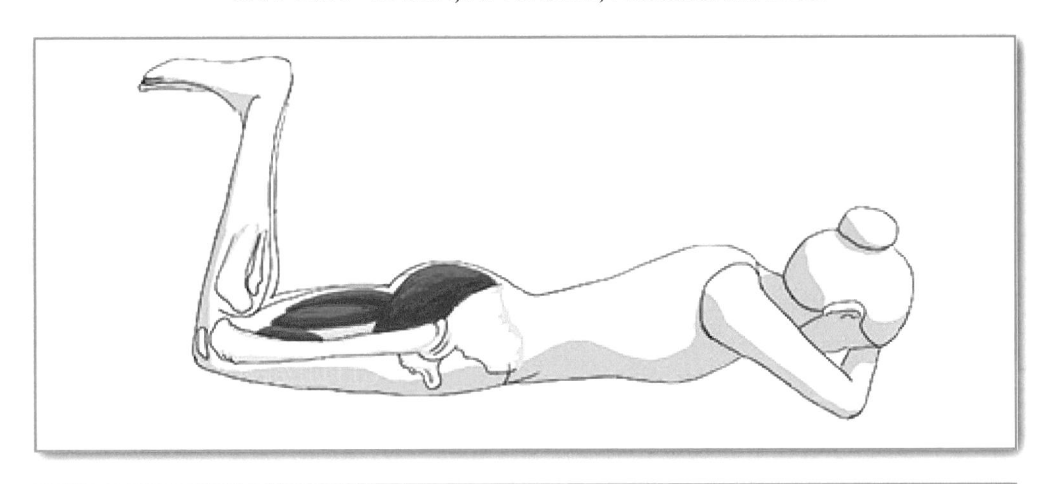

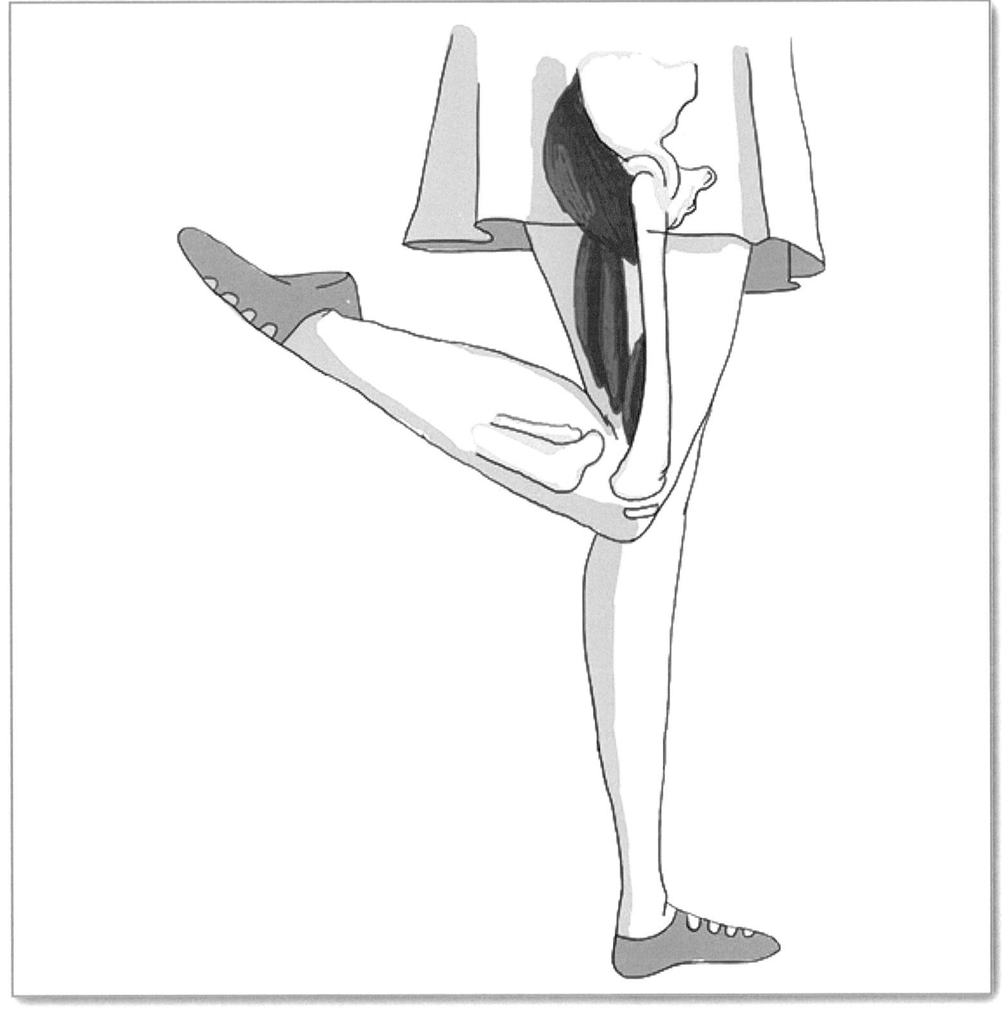

FIGURE 7.17: HAMSTRING CURL – MUSCLES USED: BICEPS FEMORIS, SEMITENDINOSUS, SEMIMEMBRANOSUS AND GLUTEUS MAXIMUS

SIDE LYING SCISSOR

PURPOSE

Muscles such as the adductors are often ignored when designing a strength training programme. This could be because you never knew they existed or maybe you did not understand their real importance. While adductors are not very effective above 50–60°, they are very adept below that level. Irish dancers use their adductors frequently by constantly crossing their feet and placing one knee in front of the other. Performing trebles (the dancer makes sounds with their foot) in your heavy dance routines also requires you to use your adductors. Get to know this exercise, practice it often and always include it in your programme.

MUSCLES USED

Adductor longus, adductor brevis, adductor magnus and gracilis.

EXECUTION

Lie on your side. With your arm extended out beyond your head, rest your head on this arm. Extend both legs, whilst maintaining a neutral spine. Keep both knees directly on top of each other.

Turn out both feet and lift the top leg. Engage your core to maintain a static trunk.

Perform small inner thigh repetitions by keeping your feet turned out and bringing your heels close together, but not touching and then separating them again. You will feel your adductors, deep transverse abdominus and pelvic floor muscles contracting. These repetitions must be performed quickly, but in a controlled manner.

Do 12 repetitions.

Complete five sets.

Increase the tempo as you advance.

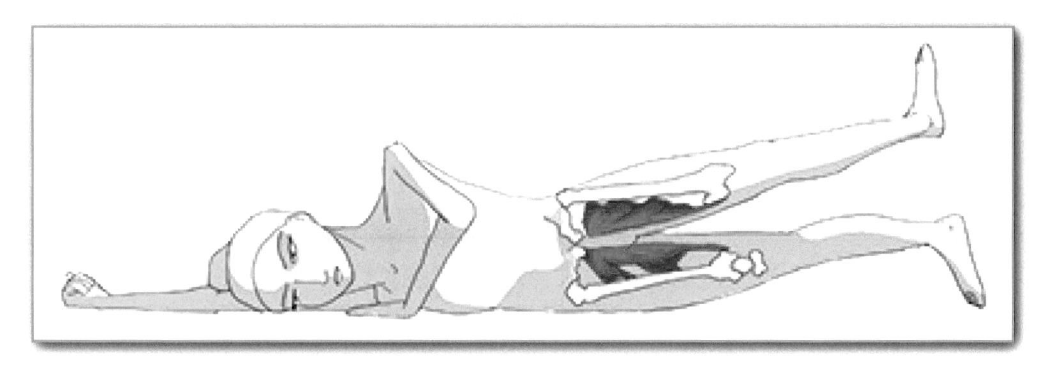

FIGURE 7.18: SIDE LYING SCISSOR – MUSCLES USED: ADDUCTOR LONGUS, ADDUCTOR BREVIS, ADDUCTOR MAGNUS AND GRACILIS

RESISTANCE BAND LEG RAISES

PURPOSE

When you are dancing, it takes great effort to perfect 'a lift' . You need to focus on power, strength, speed and control just to perform this one dancing technique. A dancer could perform the best 'lift' possible, but then the landing could be underperformed. You must have control when coming down from 'a lift' or a 'high click', so that they appear elegant. When performing the resistance band leg raises, make sure to focus on the concentric contraction of the hamstrings (shortening of the muscle), as you lower your leg. Make sure you turn out your feet and the backs of your thighs throughout the full movement. After performing this exercise, you will have a much greater range of motion and you will have more control when landing.

MUSCLES USED

Bicep femoris, semimembranosus and semitendinosus.

EXECUTION

Tie your resistance band in a knot so that it creates a circle. Loop the band around a secure object such as a table leg or a pole.

Lie on your back. Place your forefoot in the elastic band. Fully extend your leg and begin the exercise with your leg at a 90° hip flexion. Keep your foot turned out throughout the movement. Make sure your opposite leg is bent and relaxed, placing your forefoot on the ground. Stabilise your trunk when you are performing this exercise.

Exhale. Engage your abdominals to keep your back flat on the floor. Lower your leg by pushing against the resistance band with control. Lower the leg until the heel of your foot is approximately 6 inches (15 cm) from the floor.

Inhale. When returning to the starting position, raise your leg a little bit faster than when it was lowered, so that it is more realistic and reflects your dancing technique. Stabilise the trunk at all times.

Do 12 repetitions with each leg.

Complete three sets.

NOTE

Avoid pelvic tilt and spinal movement when performing this exercise.

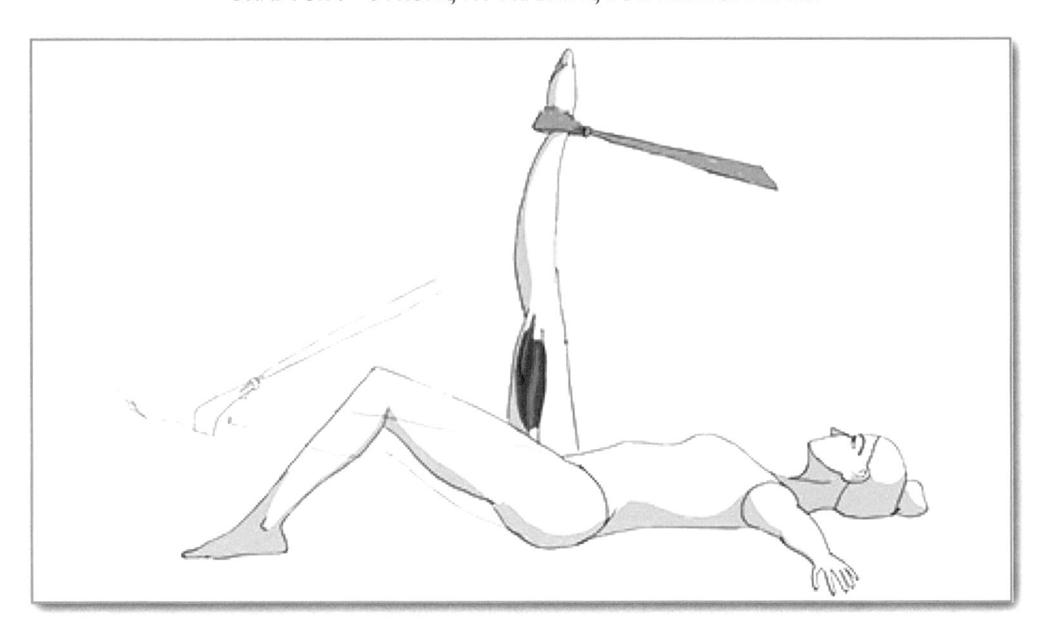

FIGURE 7.19: RESISTANCE BAND LEG RAISES – MUSCLES USED: BICEP FEMORIS, SEMIMEMBRANOSUS AND SEMITENDINOSUS

ANKLES AND FEET

As a dancer you must be able to move quickly on your feet. You must also rise up on the balls of your feet and onto your toes. You need to be able to dance in heels and pivot, or push with light pumps. Turning, jumping, pointing and tapping are basic skills needed when performing Irish dancing techniques. As a dancer you need strong and well-balanced feet and ankles, not only to provide a foundation for the whole body, but also to prevent injury.

While executing these next series of exercises, visualise your steps and understand how these movements come into play. Try to repeat them using various speeds and work rates, with 100% control throughout the entire range of motion.

DOMING

PURPOSE

This exercise strengthens the small muscles in the soles of your feet. These muscles play a significant role in pointing your toes and when you are pushing off for jumps.

MUSCLES USED

Intrinsic foot muscles.

EXECUTION

You can perform this exercise while seated. Using two small rolled-up towels, place the forefoot (the front part of your foot) on one towel and the heel of the same foot on the other towel. Make sure that your foot is balanced evenly across your toes and your heel.

Lift all toes upward at the same time, without taking your forefoot off the towel. Next slowly place them evenly on the towel again. Then push your toes downward towards the towel, again keeping your forefoot and heel on both towels at all times. Do not deliberately curl your toes.

Repeat 20 times, working your way up to higher repetitions as you get stronger.

Complete three sets.

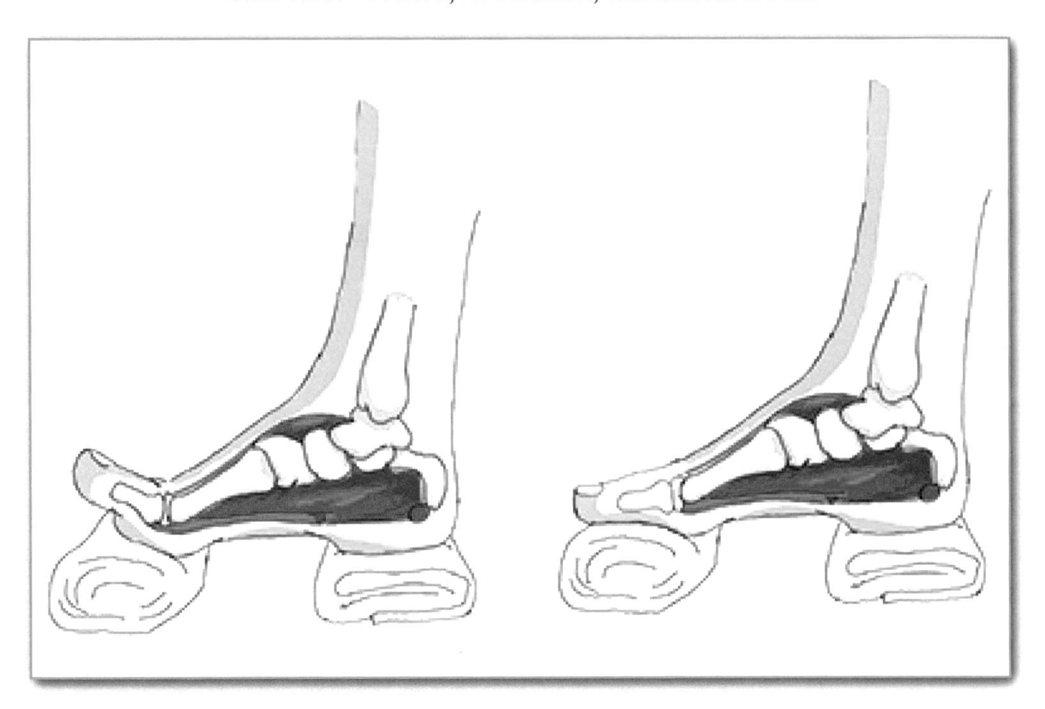

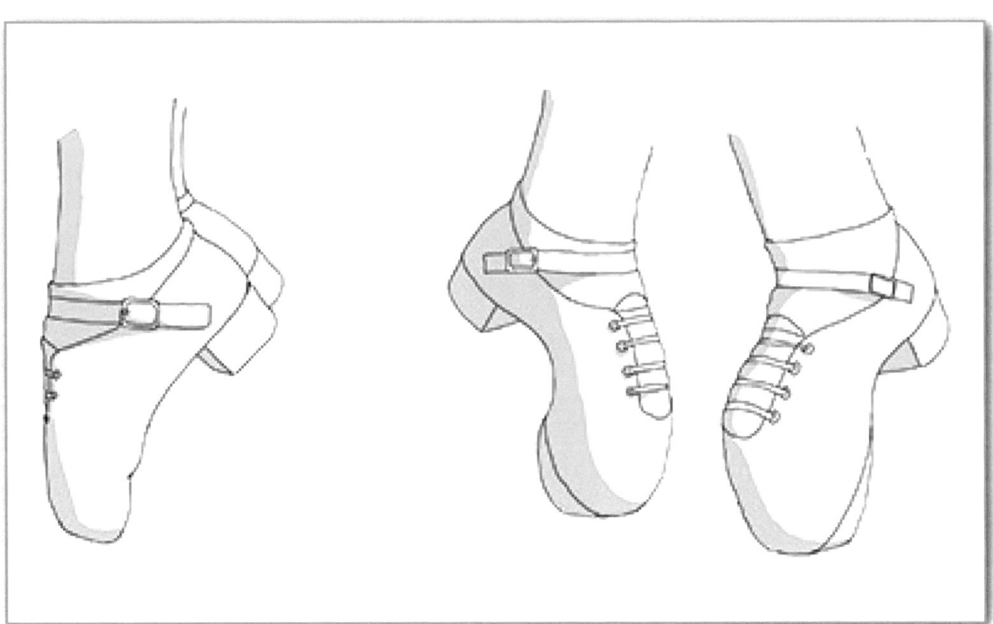

FIGURE 7.20: DOMING – MUSCLES USED: INTRINSIC FOOT MUSCLES

RESISTED INVERSION

PURPOSE

Strengthening the tibialis posterior tendon will help provide stability to the feet and ankles when landing from jumps. This will help to give you much softer and smoother landings.

MUSCLES USED

Tibialis posterior.

EXECUTION

Wrap a resistance band around the sole of your foot. Pull your forefoot inward against the resistance of the band.

Complete the full range of motion. This exercise must be performed whilst pointing your toes downward and in a flexed position.

Be sure to avoid overstretching the outside of your ankle.

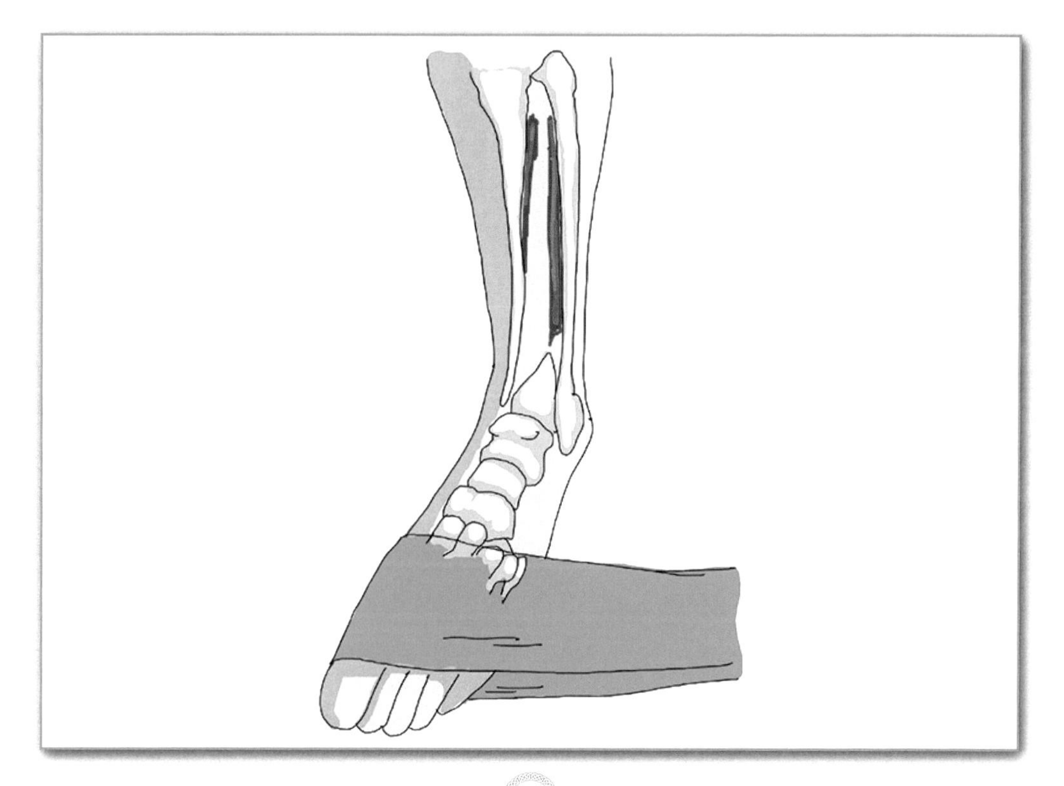

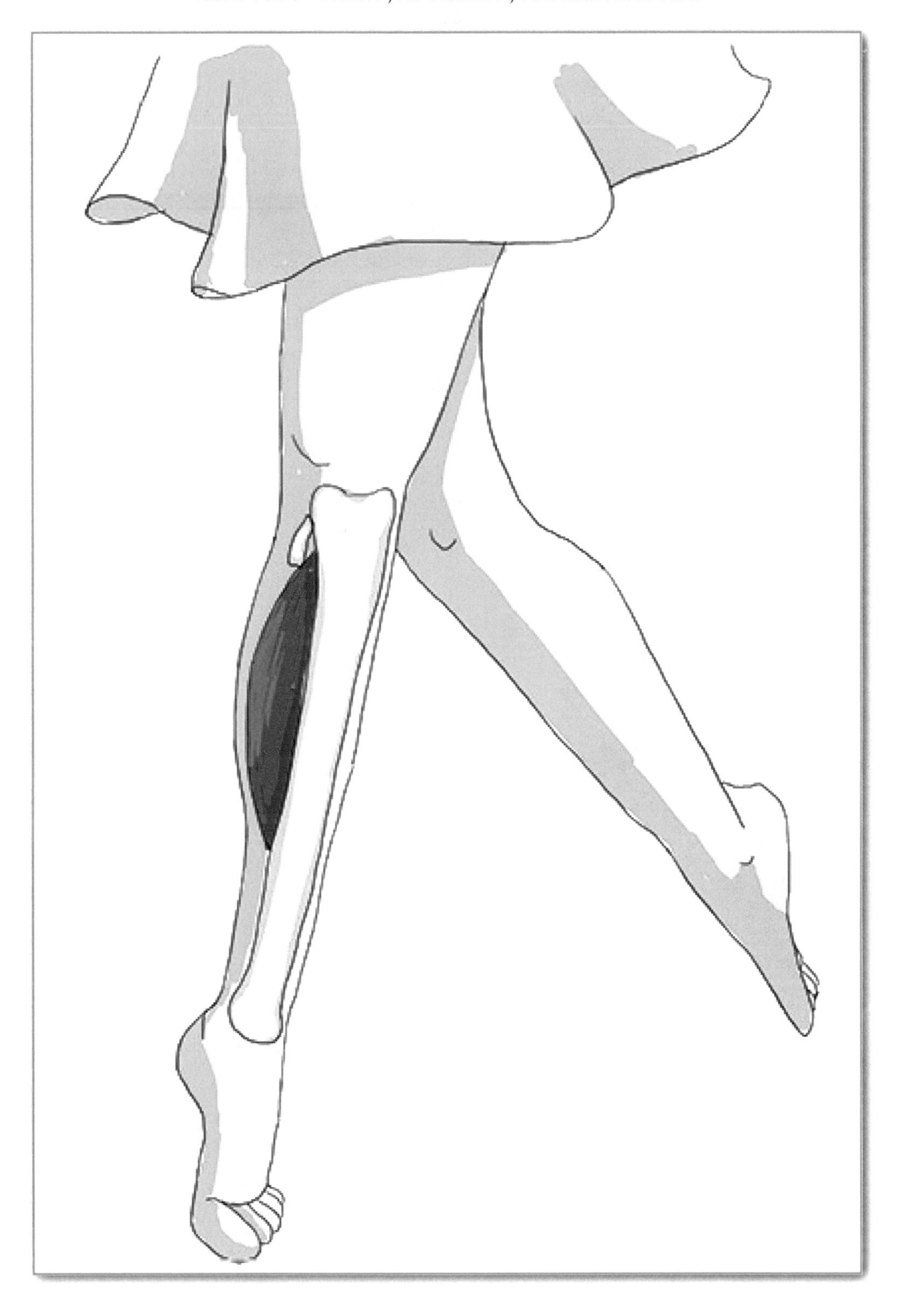

FIGURE 7.21: RESISTED INVERSION – MUSCLES USED: TIBIALIS POSTERIOR

WINGING

PURPOSE

If the peroneus muscles are lacking in strength, then there is a higher risk that you will twist your ankle, which would leave your joint unstable. This exercise will help to strengthen these muscles. When performing a 'rocking' technique, you need an excessive range of motion. Therefore you must ensure that there is enough support to avoid twisting your ankle or overstretching your ligaments. If you have suffered from an ankle sprain or strain in the past, then the chances of the injury reoccuring are much higher, so you must strengthen the peroneus muscles.

MUSCLES USED

Peroneus longus and peroneus brevis.

EXECUTION

You can perform this exercise whilst seated. Wrap a tied resistance band around the forefoot of both feet. Push the forefeet outward against the resistance of the band and return slowly.

Complete this exercise, whilst keeping your toes pointed and in a flexed position.

Repeat 20 times, working your way up as you get stronger.

Complete three sets.

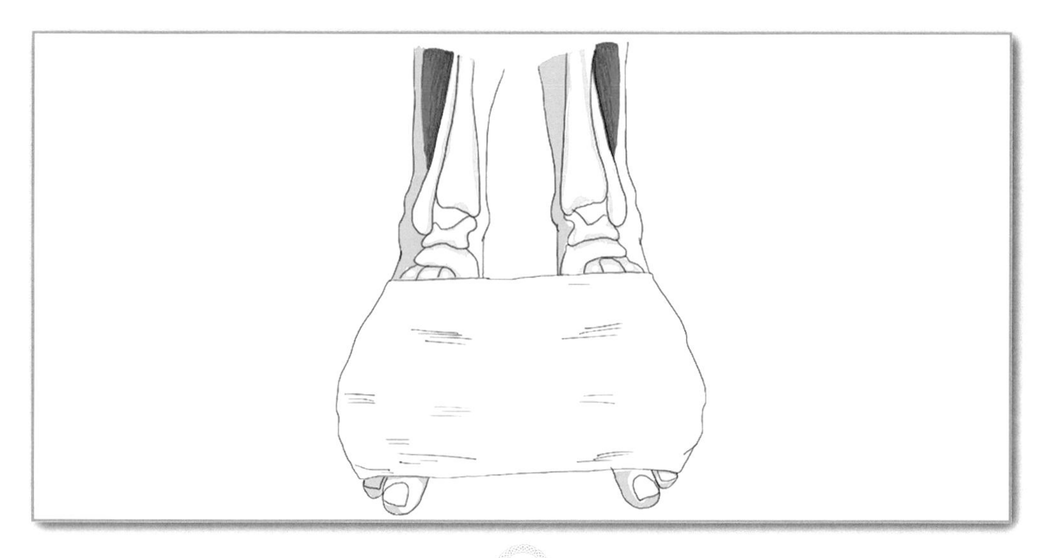

MUSCLES USED: PERONEUS LONGUS AND PERONEUS BREVIS

CALF RAISES WITH A BALL

PURPOSE

You will need strength in the lateral lower leg, the gastrocnemius and soleus to perform any dance technique that requires you to push off horizontally. While most dancers expend great effort jumping or pushing off, they have no control in the landing phase and simply let gravity take control. This can result in the dancer losing balance, leading to ankle sprains or strains. You must have adequate strength to be able to hold the horizontal position in the landing phase, as well as the take-off phase.

MUSCLES USED

Gastrocnemius, soleus, peroneus longus and peroneus brevis.

EXECUTION

With your legs in a parallel position, place a small ball between your heels. Make sure that your trunk is in a neutral position.

From a flat-footed stance, slowly raise up your toes. Hold for three seconds before returning slowly to this stance.

Repeat 20 times, working your way up as you get stronger.

Complete three sets.

NOTE

As you get much stronger you can perform single leg raises, whilst you continue to hold the ball.

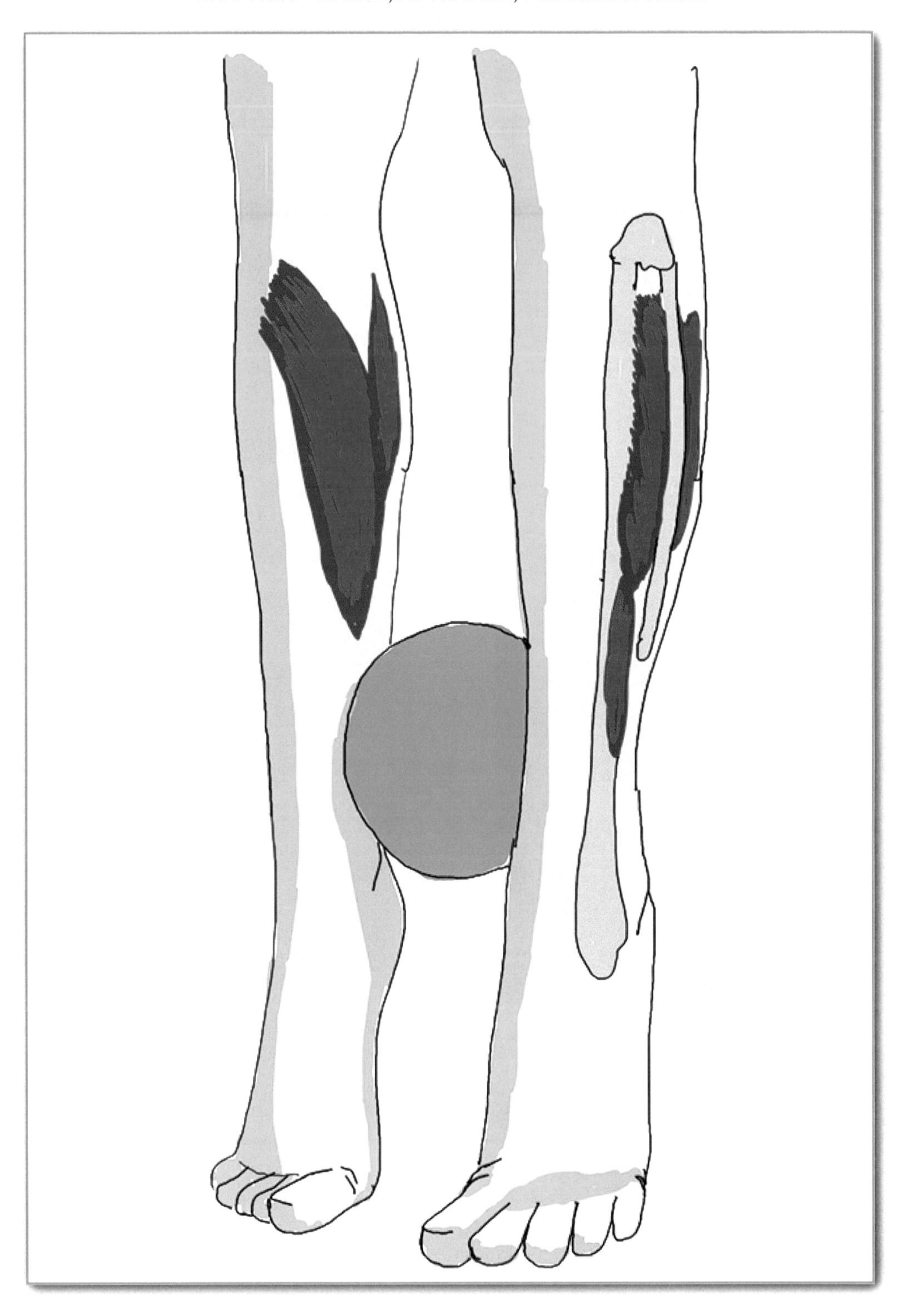

FIGURE 7.23: CALF RAISES WITH A BALL – MUSCLES USED: GASTROCNEMIUS, SOLEUS, PERONEUS LONGUS AND PERONEUS BREVIS

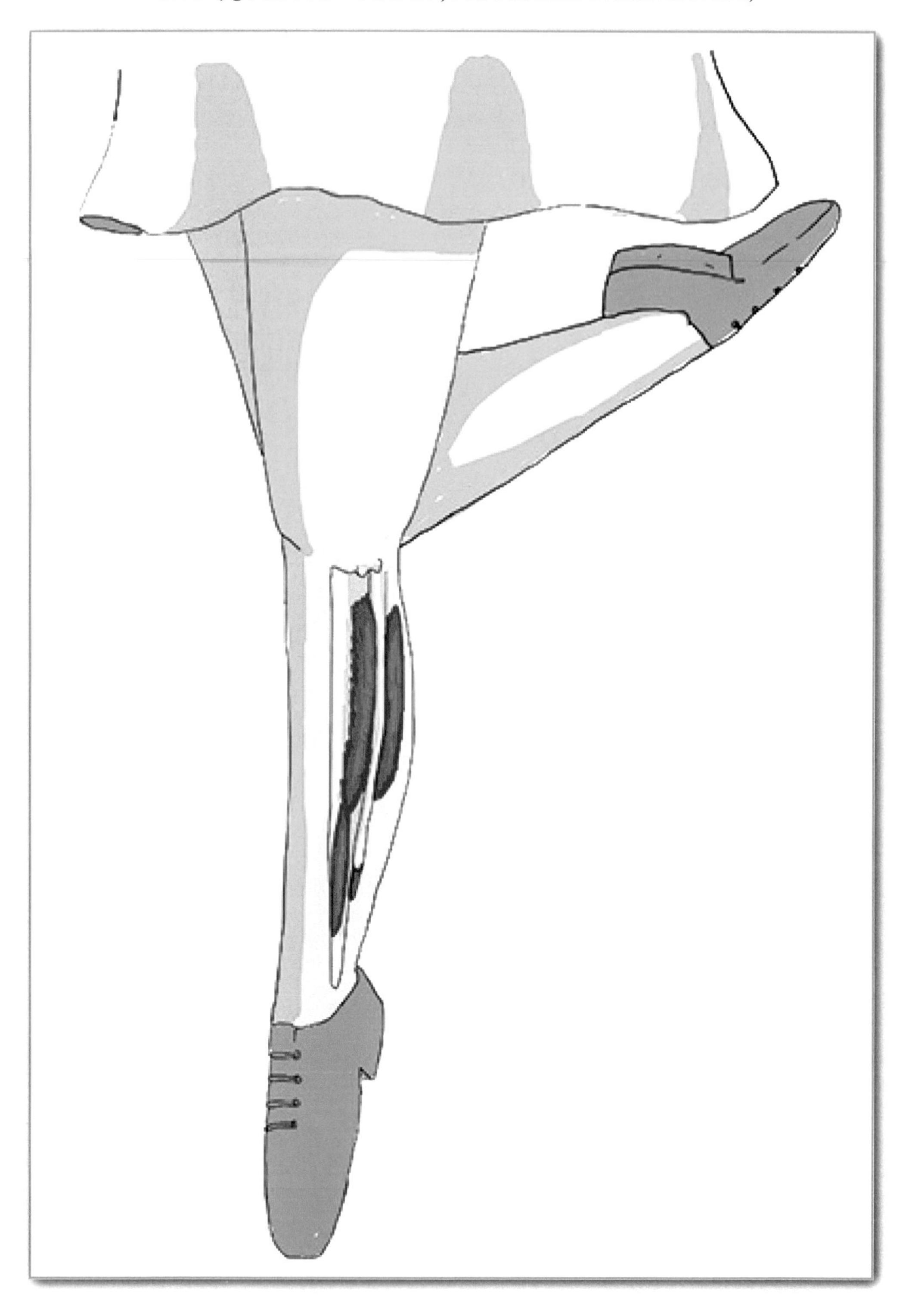

FIGURE 7.23: CALF RAISES WITH A BALL – MUSCLES USED: GASTROCNEMIUS, SOLEUS, PERONEUS LONGUS AND PERONEUS BREVIS

ANKLE DORSIFLEXION

PURPOSE

Strengthening the muscles at the front of the tibia bone gives you more stability when dancing or turning on your heels. It can also reduce the risk of shin splints.

MUSCLES USED

Tibialis anterior, extensor digitorum longus, extensor halluces longus and peroneus tertius.

EXECUTION

You can perform this exercise while seated. Wrap a tied resistance band around your forefoot. The band must be stabilised in front of you.

Begin the exercise by softly pointing your toes. Lift your toes against the resistance band and flex the ankle.

Hold for three seconds and return slowly to the starting position.

Repeat 20 times, working your way up as you get stronger.

Complete three sets.

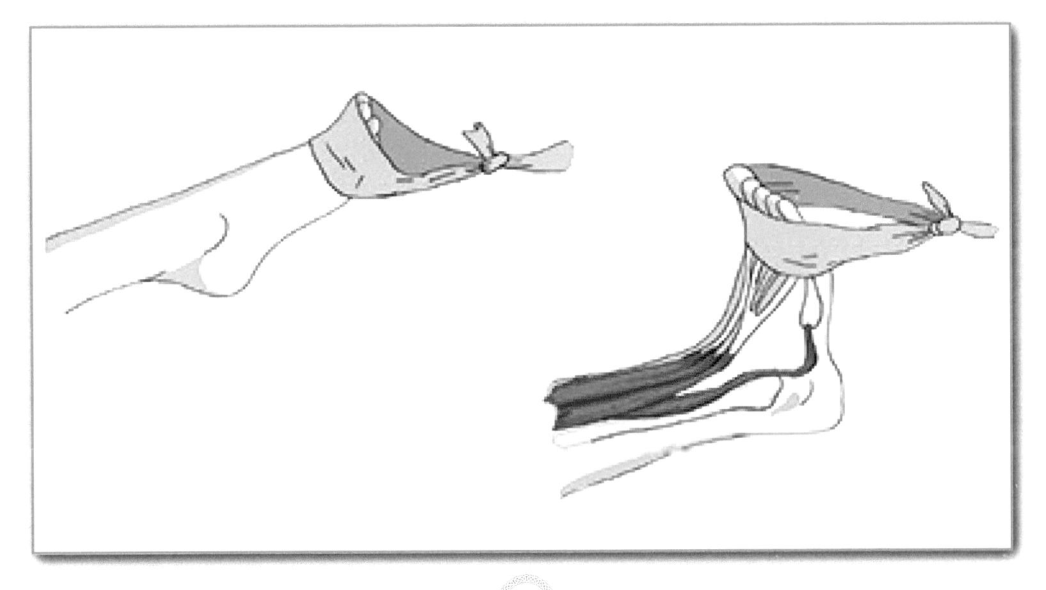

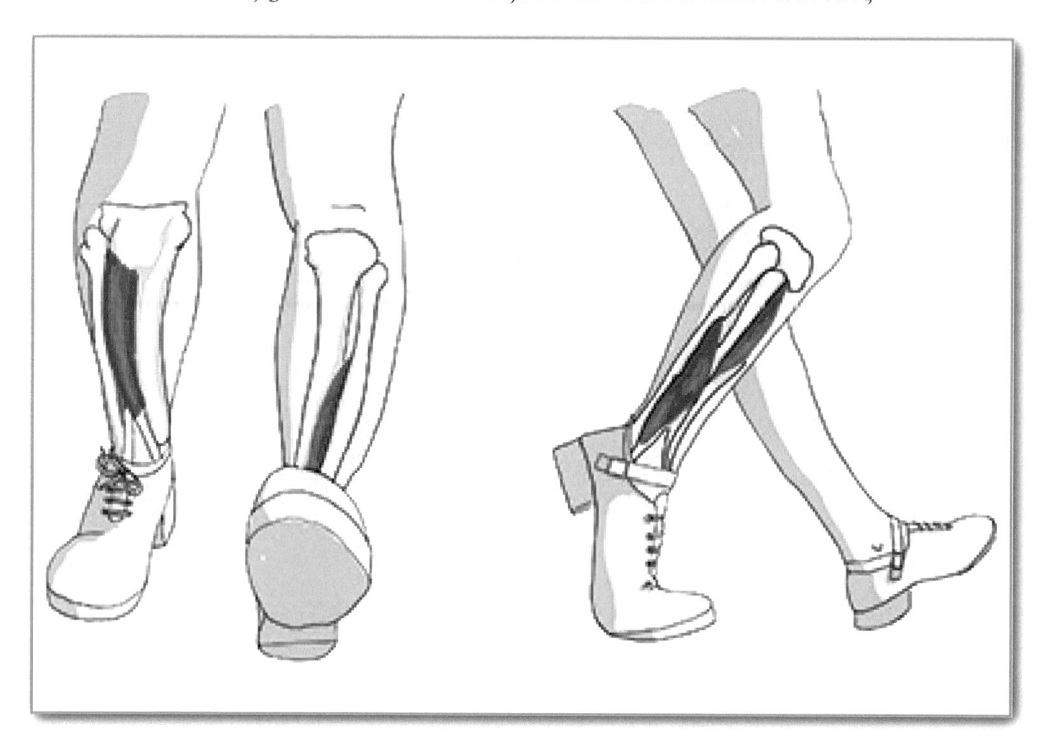

FIGURE 7.24: ANKLE DORSIFLEXION – MUSCLES USED: TIBIALIS ANTERIOR, EXTENSOR DIGITORUM LONGUS, EXTENSOR HALLUCES LONGUS AND PERONEUS TERTIUS

CHAPTER 8
BALANCE TRAINING

Balance is the body's ability to maintain its centre of gravity, while minimising postural sway. While balance is one of a dancer's most important skills, it receives the least amount of attention. It is also a key component of fitness, similar to other elements such as strength, endurance and flexibility.

Balance is not only a static process but it is also dynamic. For example, standing in one position for long periods of time is static, while multiple joint movements such as running, or even dancing, is dynamic. Daily activities such as climbing a stairs can then be considered to be both static and dynamic. It requires static foot placement, as well as multiple joint dynamic movements. To achieve these movements depends on the relationship between the muscular, neural and articular systems, also known as the kinetic chain. Balance has been proven to decrease the chances of ankle sprains and improve postural control. By including a balance training programme in your current fitness regime, you can enhance your muscle coordination, increase body awareness, contribute to joint stability and improve your reaction time in as little as 6–8 weeks. Fortunately, you do not need a lot of equipment. You can perform balance training exercises by simply using your own body weight. Improving your balance will not only enhance your dancing performance, but it will also reduce the risk of injury.

Irish dancers are required to constantly jump, and as a result, many sustain ankle inversion sprains. Not only is it a traumatising experience, but it also requires long resting periods, depending on the severity of the injury. When you sprain your ankle for the first time, the chances of the injury reoccurring are much higher due to instability. Therefore, you must strongly focus on preventing such injuries from occurring in the first place, or else prevent them from reoccurring. You can do this by including balance training in your current regime to improve stability and increase postural control.

When designing an integrated balance training programme, as is the case with all other programmes, it is important to ensure that you choose exercises that are safe, while also challenging. Make sure they are progressive, functional and carried out in a suitable environment.

BALANCE TRAINING: STABILISATION

We will now focus on exercises that require very little joint motion. These activities mainly concentrate on stabilising the joints to prepare the body to react and contract the correct muscles when operating in an unstable environment.

SINGLE LEG BALANCE

Placing your hands on your hips, keep your body in an upright position. Engage your core (that is, stiffen the core muscles around your abdomen) and bend your knees slightly.

Lift your left foot off the ground. Hold for up to 20 seconds and return to the starting position in a controlled manner.

Repeat with the opposite leg.

Complete three sets.

FIGURE 8.1: SINGLE LEG BALANCE – SINGLE LEG BALANCE ON A PILLOW OR SOFT FOAM ROLL

Placing your hands on your hips, keep your body in an upright position. Engage your core and bend your knees slightly.

Stand on a pillow or foam roll with your left foot. Hold for up to 20 seconds and return to the starting position in a controlled manner.

Repeat with the opposite leg.

Complete three sets.

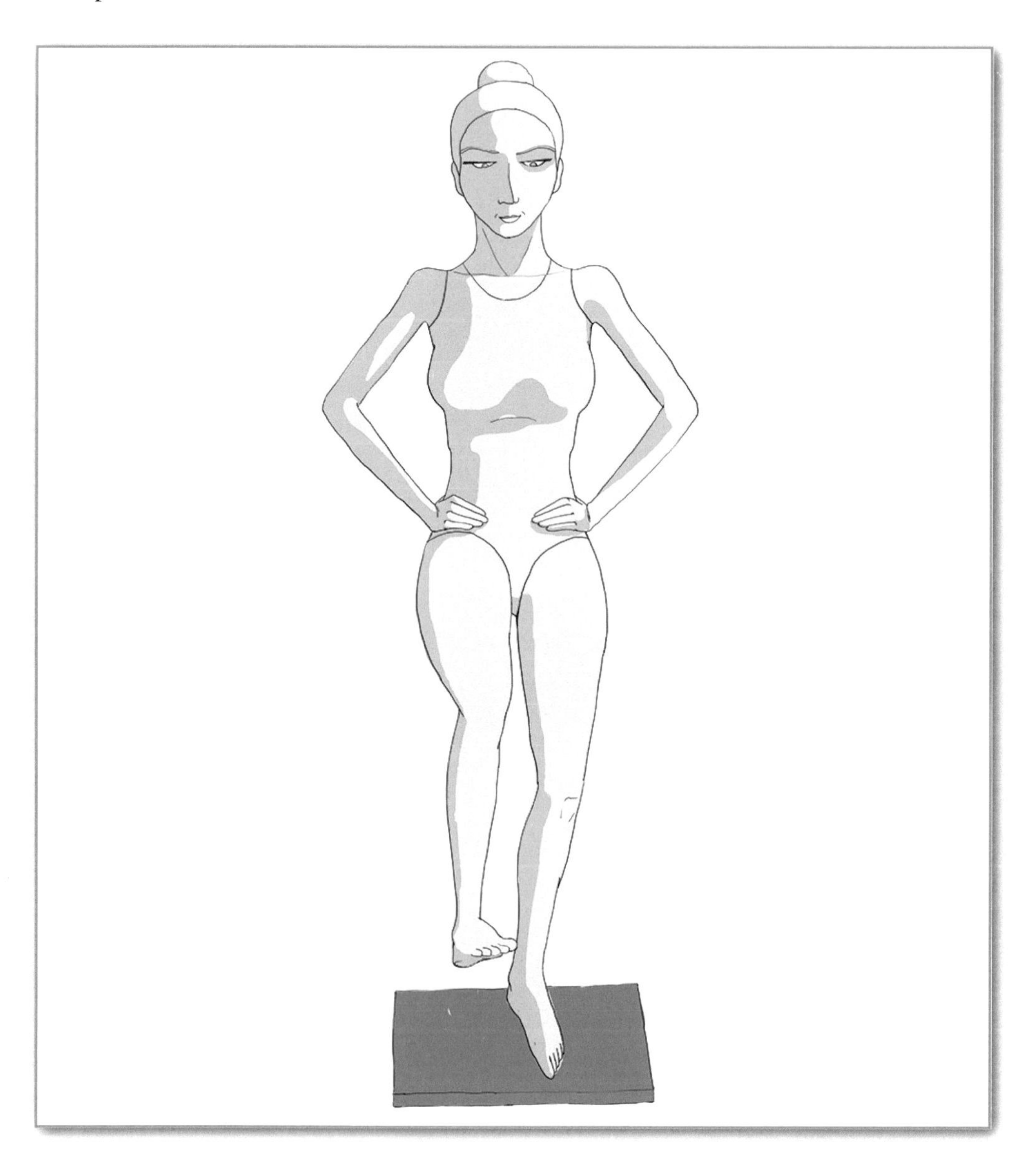

FIGURE 8.2: SINGLE LEG BALANCE ON A PILLOW OR SOFT FOAM ROLL

SINGLE LEG REACH: TO THE FRONT OF THE BODY

Placing your hands on your hips, keep your body in an upright position. Engage your core and bend your knees slightly.

Point your toe and fully extend your right knee, keeping your leg almost parallel with the opposite leg. Hold for up to 20 seconds and return to the starting position in a controlled manner.

Repeat with the opposite leg.

Complete three sets.

FIGURE 8.3: SINGLE LEG REACH: TO THE FRONT OF THE BODY

SINGLE LEG REACH: TO THE SIDE OF THE BODY

Placing your hands on your hips, keep your body in an upright position. Engage your core and bend your knees slightly.

Point your toe and fully extend your left knee, lifting your leg up to your left side. Hold for up to 20 seconds and return in a controlled manner.

Repeat with the opposite leg.

Complete three sets.

FIGURE 8.4: SINGLE LEG REACH: TO THE SIDE OF THE BODY

SINGLE LEG REACH: BEHIND THE BODY

Placing your hands on your hips, keep your body in an upright position. Engage your core and bend your knees slightly.

Point your toe and fully extend your left leg. Lift your leg up in a hyperextended fashion, whilst slightly rotating your hips. Hold for up to 20 seconds and return in a controlled manner.

Complete three sets.

FIGURE 8.5: SINGLE LEG REACH: BEHIND THE BODY

BALANCE TRAINING: STRENGTH

We will now focus on exercises that include both static and dynamic processes. The pace that you perform these exercises can be increased as you progress as a dancer.

STEP-UPS

EQUIPMENT NEEDED

A secure box roughly 12–24 inches (30–60 cm) in height.

Place your hands on your hips or tightly by your sides, as when dancing. Keep your body in an upright position. Engage your core and bend your knees slightly.

Leading with your right foot, step onto the box, placing your heels safely on it. Stand upright with your hips and knees fully extended. Engage your core muscles and your gluteal muscles. Return to a starting position in a safe and controlled manner.

Do 12 repetitions with each leg.

Complete three sets.

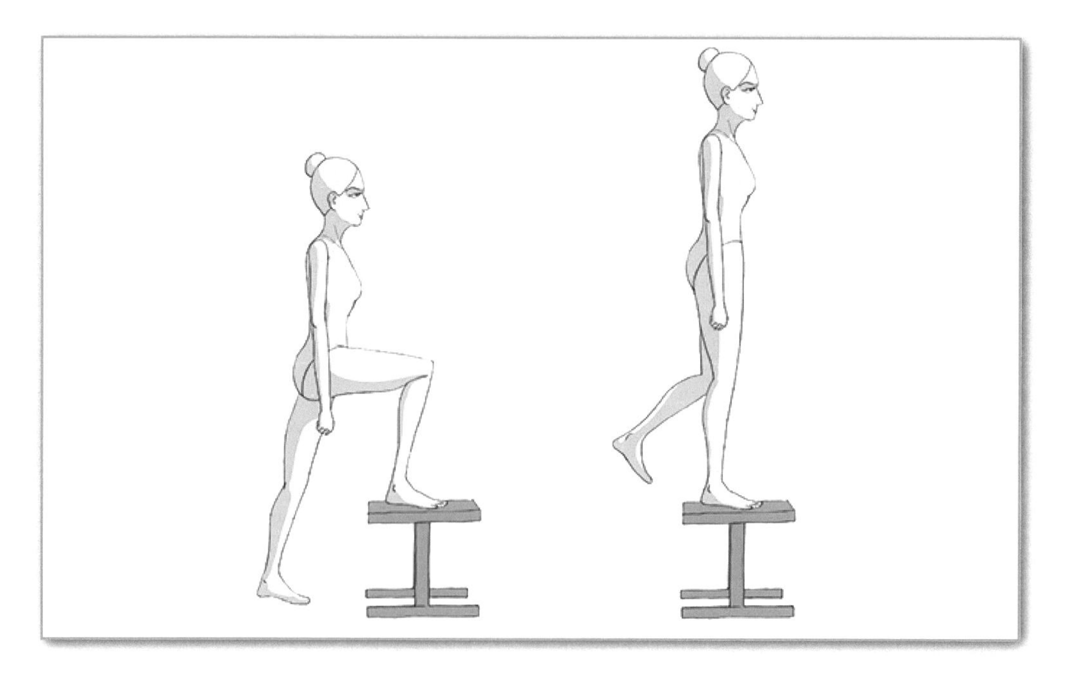

FIGURE 8.6: STEP-UPS

STEP-UP: HIGH KNEE

EQUIPMENT NEEDED

A secure box roughly 12–24 inches (30–60 cm) in height.

Place your hands on your hips or tightly by your sides, as when dancing. Keeping your body in an upright position, engage your core and bend your knees slightly.

Leading with your right foot, step onto the box, placing your heel safely on it. Stand upright with your hips fully extended and lift your left knee towards your chest. Engage your core muscles and gluteal muscles. Return to the starting position in a safe and controlled manner.

Do 12 repetitions with each leg.

Complete three sets.

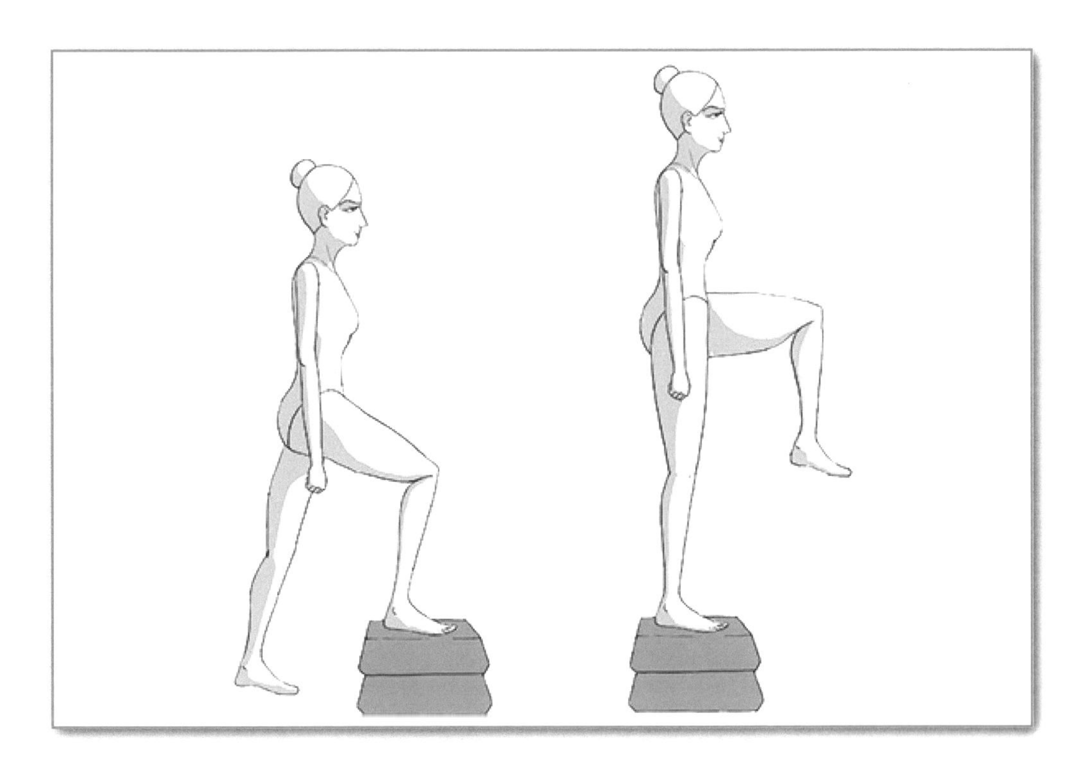

FIGURE 8.7: STEP-UP: HIGH KNEE

STEP-UP: TURNING WITH HIGH KNEE

EQUIPMENT NEEDED

A secure box roughly 12–24 inches (30–60 cm) in height.

Stand sideways beside the box. Place your hands on your hips or tightly by your sides, as when dancing. Keep your body in an upright position. Engage your core and bend your knees slightly.

Place your left foot onto the box. Turn your body to face the box. Lift your body onto the box, using your left leg and raise your right knee to your chest. Return to the starting position in a safe and controlled manner.

Do 12 repetitions with each leg.

Complete three sets.

FIGURE 8.8: STEP-UP: TURNING WITH HIGH KNEE

BALANCE TRAINING: POWER

Now, we will focus on exercises that require stabilisation, strength and dynamic neuromuscular efficiency (the nervous system's ability to mobilise the correct muscles to create and reduce force, as well as to dynamically stabilise the body's structure).

SINGLE LEG HOP

Placing your hands on your hips, keep your body in an upright position. Engage your core and bend your knees slightly.

Lift your right foot off the ground and jump as far as you can, pushing off your left foot and landing on your left foot. Try to avoid resting your right foot on the ground.

Repeat with the opposite leg.

Do 12 repetitions with each leg.

Complete three sets.

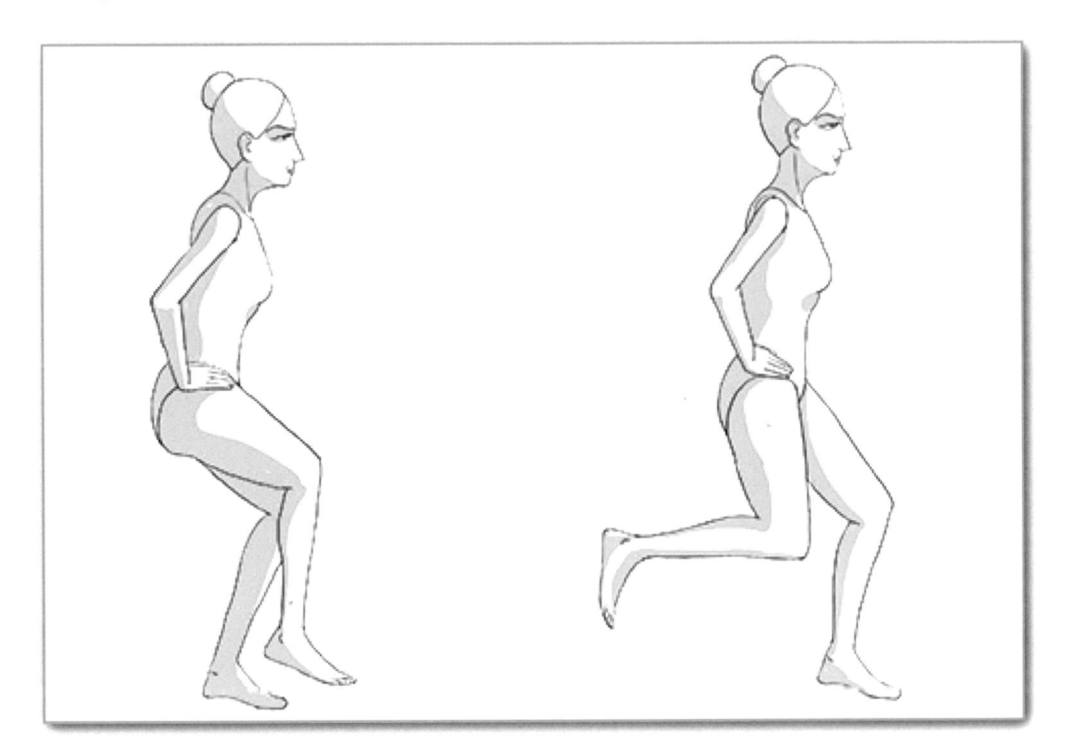

FIGURE 8.9: SINGLE LEG HOP

SINGLE LEG BOX JUMP

EQUIPMENT NEEDED

A secure box roughly 12–24 inches (30–60 cm) in height.

NOTE

This jump requires a considerable amount of strength, coordination and balance. It is only recommended for advanced athletes. If you are introducing this exercise into your programme for the first time, I recommend that you set the box at an appropriate height. An appropriate height is when you find it comfortable and easy to do.

Place your hands by your sides and bend your knees slightly. Explode upwards, pushing off the balls of your feet. Raise your knees to your chest and land on the box softly with one foot. Stand up straight on the box, with your hips fully extended and your body upright. Next, rest both of your feet. Step down off the box safely, do not jump down.

Repeat with the opposite leg.

Do 12 repetitions with each leg.

Complete three sets.

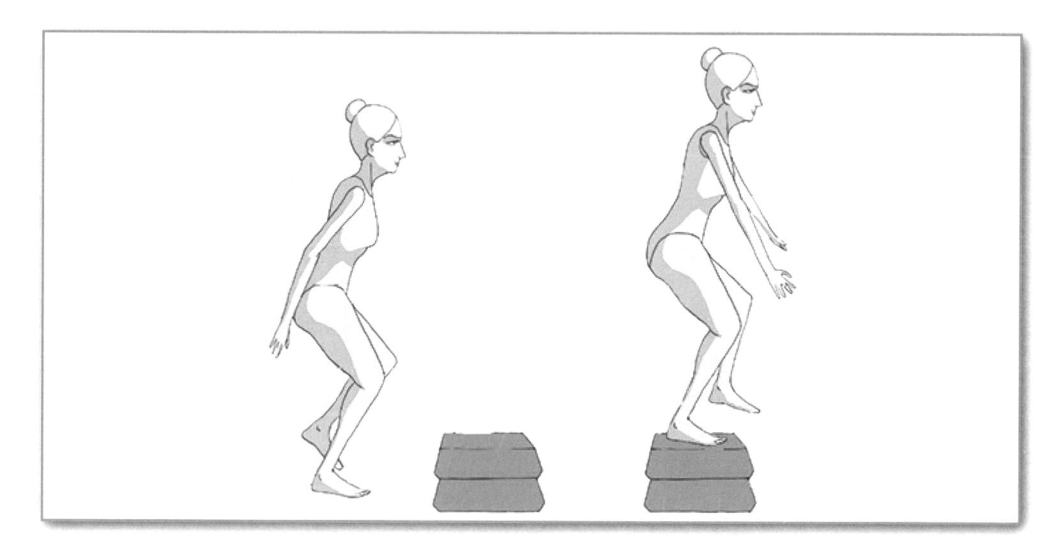

FIGURE 8.10: SINGLE LEG BOX JUMP

SINGLE LEG HOP DOWN

EQUIPMENT NEEDED

A secure box roughly 12–24 inches (30–60 cm) in height.

Place your hands by your sides. Standing on the box, bend your knees slightly and lift your left foot off the box, balancing on your right foot. Jump from the box to the ground, landing on your left foot.

Repeat with the opposite leg.

Do 12 repetitions with each leg.

Complete three sets.

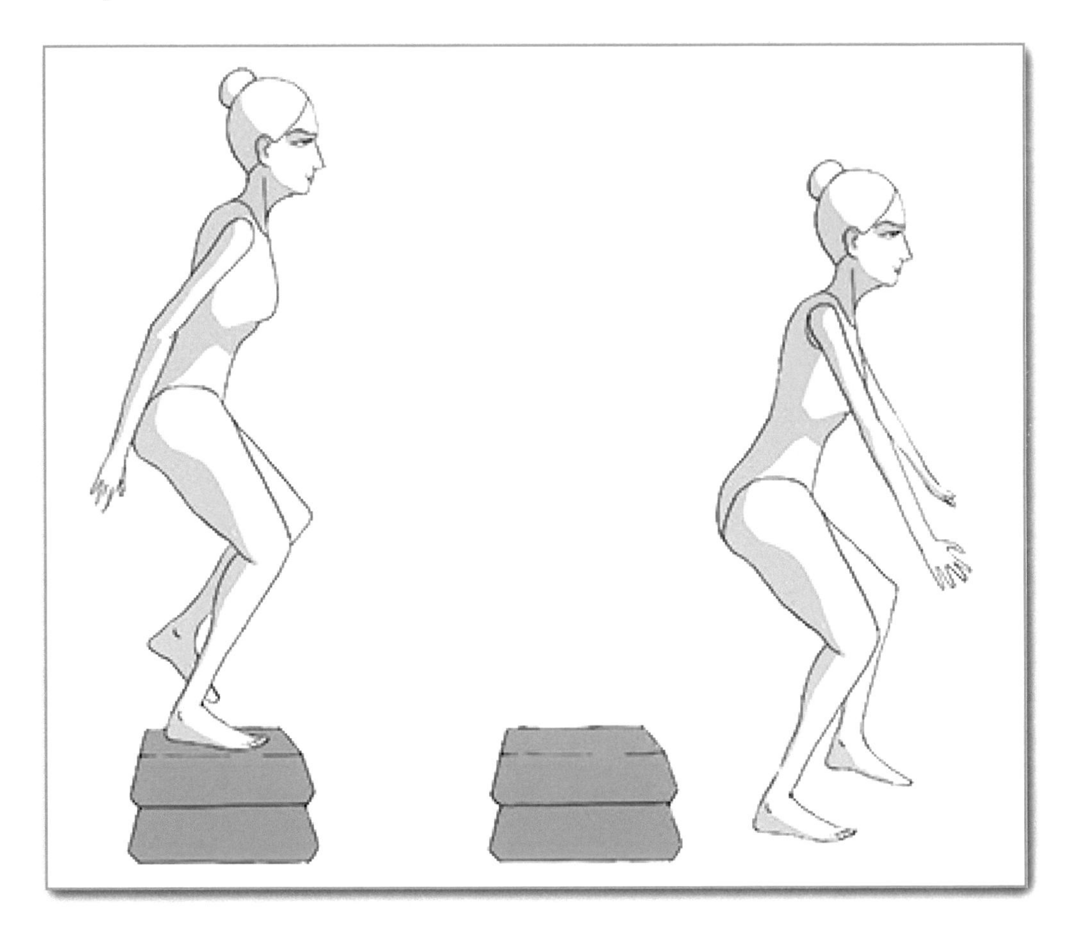

FIGURE 8.11: SINGLE LEG HOP DOWN

CHAPTER 9
FLEXIBILITY

Flexibility is basically the ability to stretch and elongate muscles smoothly and easily, through the available range of motion. I referred to stretching in Chapter 6 on warm-ups and cool-downs, but here I will elaborate on the different exercises in more detail. I will briefly discuss their advantages and disadvantages. In addition, I will advise on when to stretch, what muscles to use and how often you should do this. Good flexibility is just as important for dancers as strength. Muscles must be strong, but they also have to be long to work optimally.

DYNAMIC AND STATIC STRETCHING

Flexibility can be divided into two components: dynamic and static. In its simplest form, dynamic flexibility is the body's ability to move its joints, by contracting the muscles and using the available active range of motion. Static stretching is the ability to elongate a muscle, while the body is at rest. The main focus is to hold a position of a joint or muscle that is minimally challenging, relaxing the body part being stretched and increasing the stretch as far it allows you to.

DYNAMIC STRETCHING

Dynamic stretching is not as effective as static stretching in the long-term, but it is more beneficial to you in getting your body ready for an activity. Dynamic stretching techniques are used only after a warm-up routine. You must ensure that your body is at the right temperature before performing dynamic stretching exercises. If you are trying to guess whether your body is at the correct temperature before performing this routine, working up to a light sweat is always a good indication. You should start with slow movements and gradually increase their speed and power, as the body allows.

DYNAMIC STRETCHING EXERCISES

JOINT ROTATIONS

From a standing position, keep your arms in a relaxed position at your sides. Flex, extend and rotate each of the following joints:

Fingers, wrists, elbows, shoulders, neck, trunk and shoulder blades, hips, knees, ankles, feet and toes.

Do 10–12 repetitions with each joint.

MOBILITY EXERCISES: UPPER BODY

ARM SWINGS

FORWARD / BACKWARD

Swing both arms continuously into an overhead position, in a slow and controlled motion, and then forward, downward and backward.

Do 12 repetitions.

SIDE TO SIDE

Swing both arms out to your side, keeping your arms at chest height.

Do 12 repetitions in each direction.

NECK MOVEMENTS

FLEXION / EXTENSION

Tuck your chin into your chest, and then lift your chin upward, as far as possible.

Do 12 repetitions.

LATERAL FLEXION

Lower your head toward your left shoulder and then toward your right shoulder, in a slow and controlled manner.

Do 12 repetitions.

ROTATION

Perform slow movements of the head in a clockwise direction and then repeat anticlockwise.

Do 12 repetitions.

SHOULDER MOVEMENTS

SHRUGS

Keeping your arms straight and relaxed at all times, and your body in a straight upright position, simply lift your shoulders, bringing them close to your ears and back to a relaxed position.

Do 12 repetitions.

SIDE BENDS

Keeping your arms relaxed at both sides, lean to your right side and hold your legs straight, until your hand goes past your knee.

Repeat on your left side.

Do 12 repetitions.

ROTATION

Keeping your arms straight and relaxed, lift your shoulders, and bring them forward in a circular motion.

Repeat, bringing your arms backwards.

Do 12 repetitions.

MOBILITY EXERCISES: LOWER BODY

HIP MOVEMENTS

CIRCLES

With your hands on your hips and feet spread apart, wider than your shoulders, make circles with your hips in a clockwise direction. Then repeat the circles in an anticlockwise direction.

Do 12 repetitions in each direction.

TWISTS

Extend your arms out to your sides, and twist your torso and hips to the left, shifting your weight on to the left foot. Then twist your torso to the right, while shifting your weight onto the right foot.

Do 12 repetitions on each side.

LEG SWINGS

FLEXION / EXTENSION / HYPEREXTENSION

With the weight on your left leg, and your right hand on a support for balance, swing your right leg forward and backward for 12 repetitions.

Repeat with the left leg for 10–12 repetitions.

SIDE TO SIDE SWINGS

Leaning slightly forward, with your hands on a wall or pillar and your weight on your left leg, swing your right leg to the left, with your toes pointing upward and return to the starting position. Then standing with all of the weight on your right leg, swing your left leg to the right and back to the starting position.

Repeat this overall motion 12 times with each leg.

ANKLE MOVEMENTS

DOUBLE LEG BOUNCE

Leaning forward, with your hands on the wall and your weight on your toes, raise and lower both heels rapidly (bounce). Each time, lift your heels 1–2 inches (2.5–5 cm) from the ground, while maintaining ground contact with the balls of your feet.

Do 12–16 repetitions.

SINGLE LEG BOUNCE

Leaning forward, with your hands on a wall and all your weight on your left foot, raise your right knee forward, while pushing the left heel towards the ground. Then lower the right foot to the floor, while raising the left heel 1–2 inches (2.5–5 cm).

Repeat in a rapid, bouncy fashion for 12–16 repetitions, before carrying out the same number of repetitions on the opposite side.

STATIC STRETCHING

Static stretching is the most effective way to elongate a muscle to produce long-term gains. Static stretching exercises should only be performed after a workout, and there should be no movement of the joint or limb. As you stretch, there should be a slight lengthening of the muscle and you should not experience any pain or discomfort whilst doing so. If you are in any pain or discomfort, do not to continue with these exercises. Seek advice from a health professional. Once in the stretch position, hold for 30 seconds, and then relax. While you are holding, you can apply force to increase the stretch, if needed. This should be done in a controlled and steady manner. Forcing the stretch too much can cause muscle or tendon tears or strains. You may have witnessed other dancers moving their joint or limb when stretching, causing the muscle to shorten and lengthen (bouncing on the stretch). This stretching should be avoided at all times.

STATIC STRETCHING EXERCISES

UPPER BODY

NECK STRETCH

Standing tall, with your feet shoulder-width apart, or sit on a chair, keeping your back straight and your feet on the floor. Relax your shoulders and lower your head toward your right shoulder. To increase the stretch, if needed, use your right hand to put gentle pressure on your head, pushing it toward your right shoulder. Hold the stretch and then return slowly to the neutral position.

Repeat on the left side.

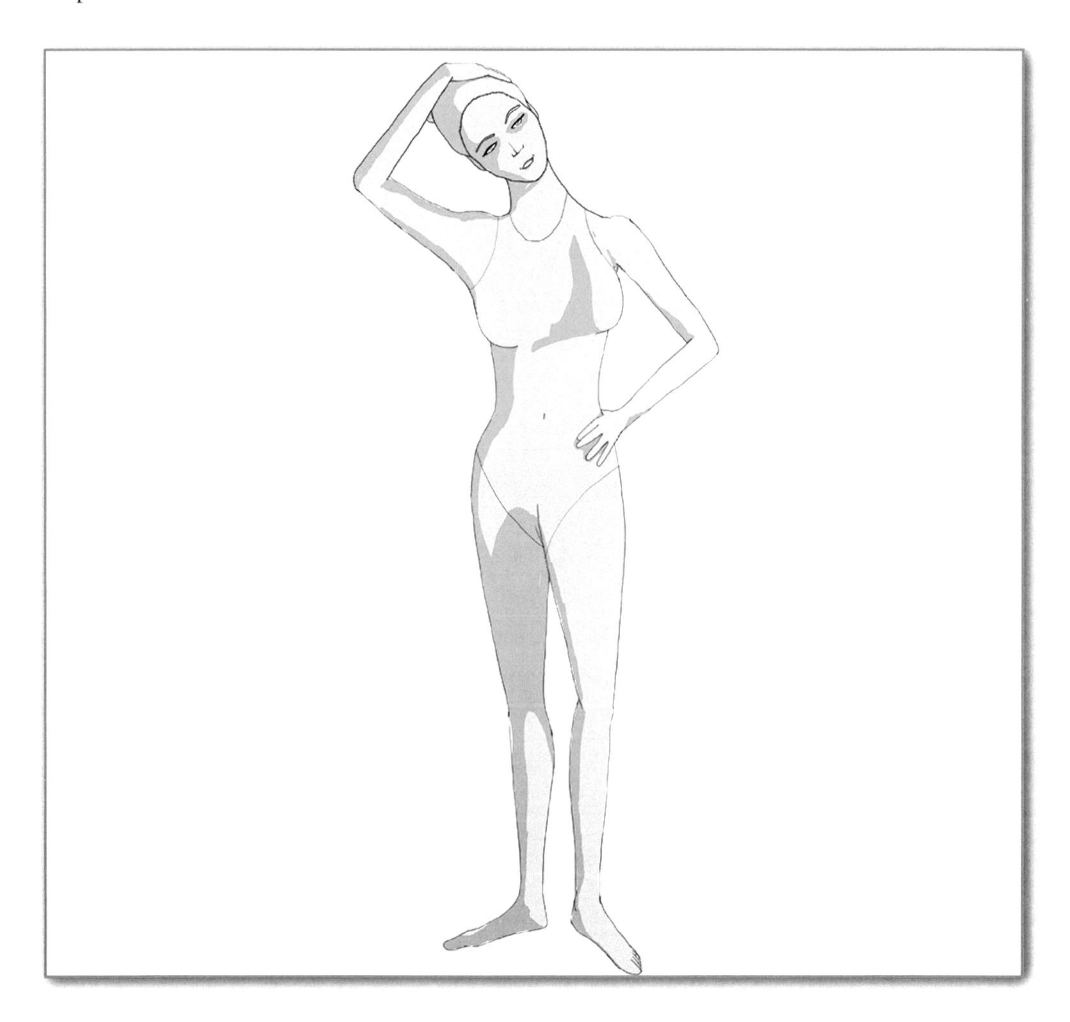

FIGURE 9.1: NECK STRETCH

CHEST STRETCH

Standing tall, with your feet wider than shoulder-width apart, hold your arms out to the side in a parallel position with the ground and your palms facing forward. Stretch your arms as far behind you as possible. You should feel the stretch across your chest. Hold until you can increase the stretch and then hold again.

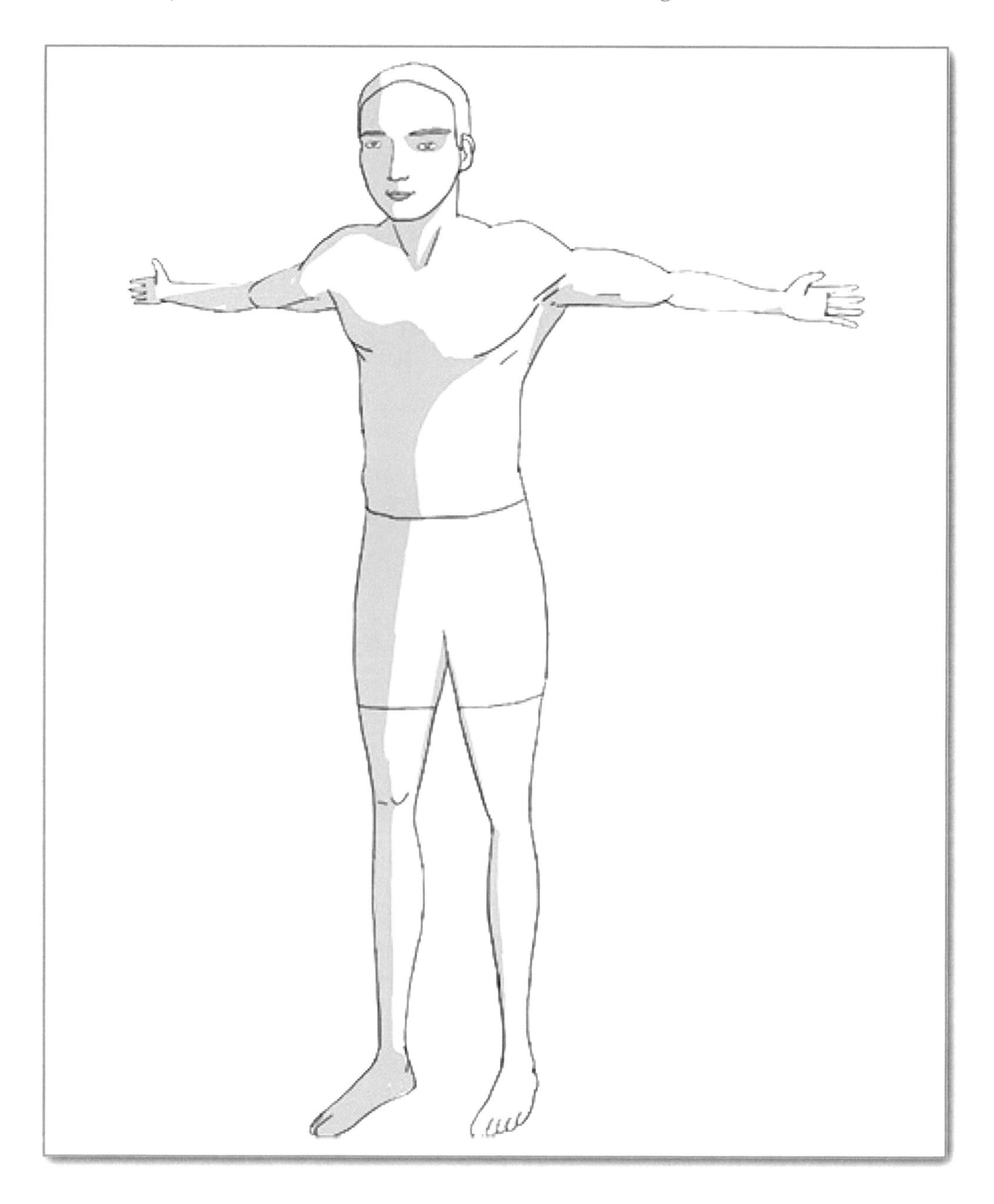

FIGURE 9.2: CHEST STRETCH

UPPER BACK STRETCH

Standing tall, with your feet wider than shoulder-width apart, knees slightly bent, interlock your fingers and push your hands as far away from your chest as possible, allowing your upper back to relax.

You should feel the stretch between your shoulder blades.

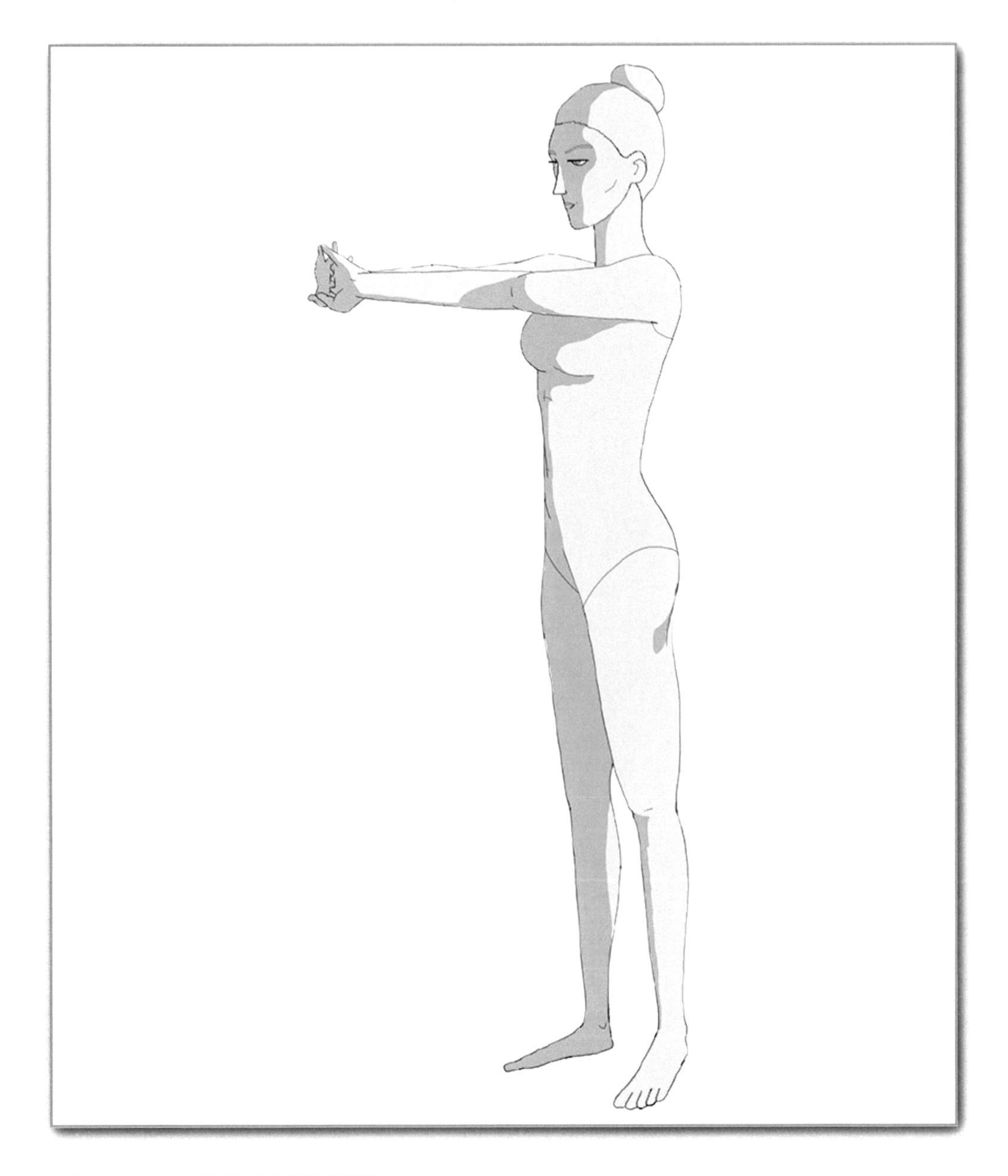

FIGURE 9.3: UPPER BACK STRETCH

SHOULDER STRETCH

Standing tall, with your feet wider than shoulder-width apart and knees slightly bent, bring your right arm to the front of your chest, parallel with the ground. Then whilst keeping your left elbow bent, bring it in front of your right arm, easing your right arm closer to your chest.

Repeat this exercise with your other arm.

FIGURE 9.4: SHOULDER STRETCH

SIDE BENDS

Standing tall, with your feet wider than shoulder-width apart, make sure your knees are slightly bent. Place your right hand at your side, and then slowly bring your right hand downward closer to your knee, until you feel a stretch on your left side. Return to a vertical position.

Repeat on the other side.

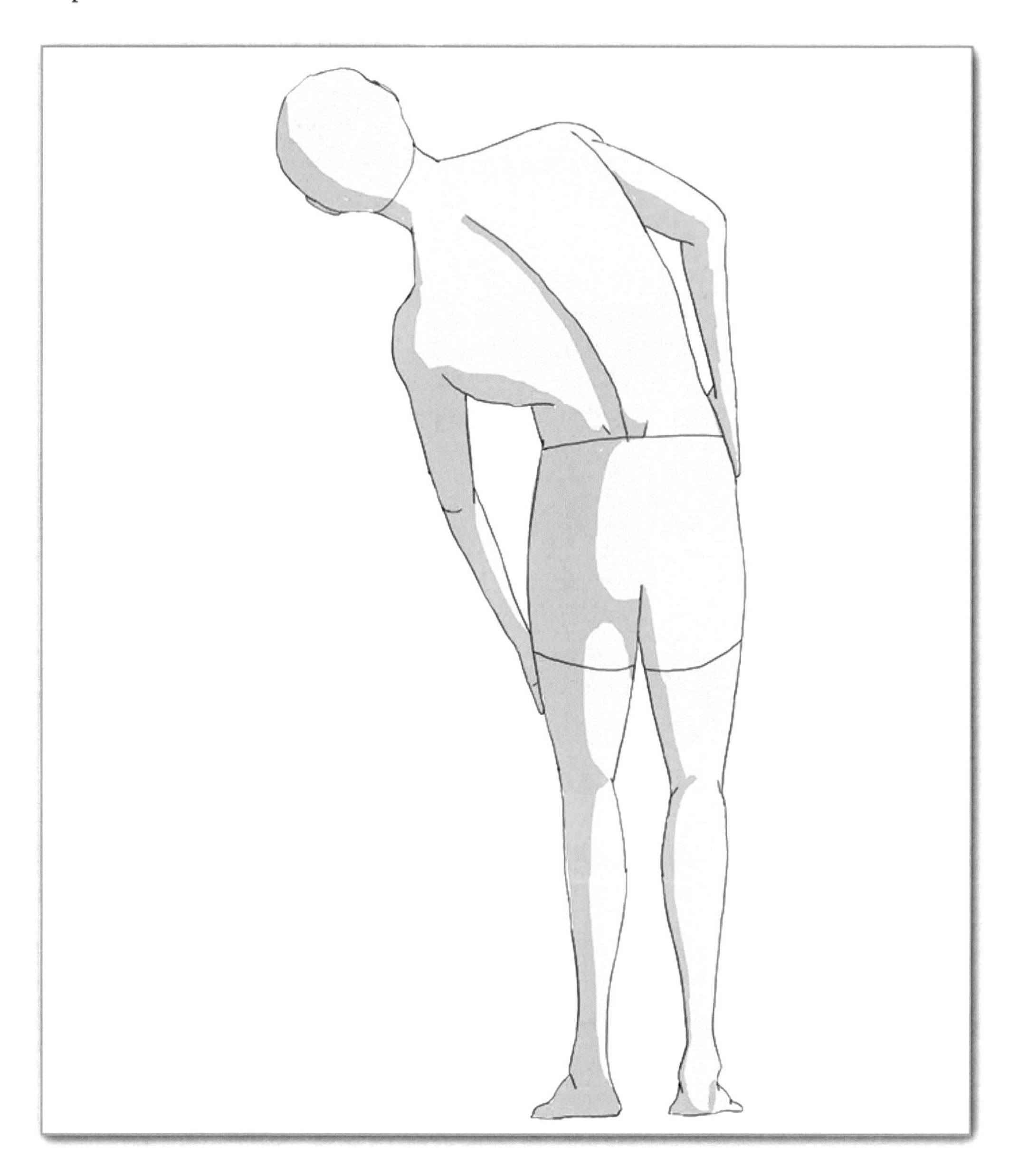

FIGURE 9.5: SIDE BENDS

ABDOMINAL STRETCH

Lie down on your front, placing your hands either side of your chest. Gently arch your neck backward towards your lower back, to a position that is comfortable. Keeping your hips on the ground, slowly straighten your arms, pressing against the floor and lifting your trunk off the ground. Relax and hold the stretch and then slowly return to the starting position.

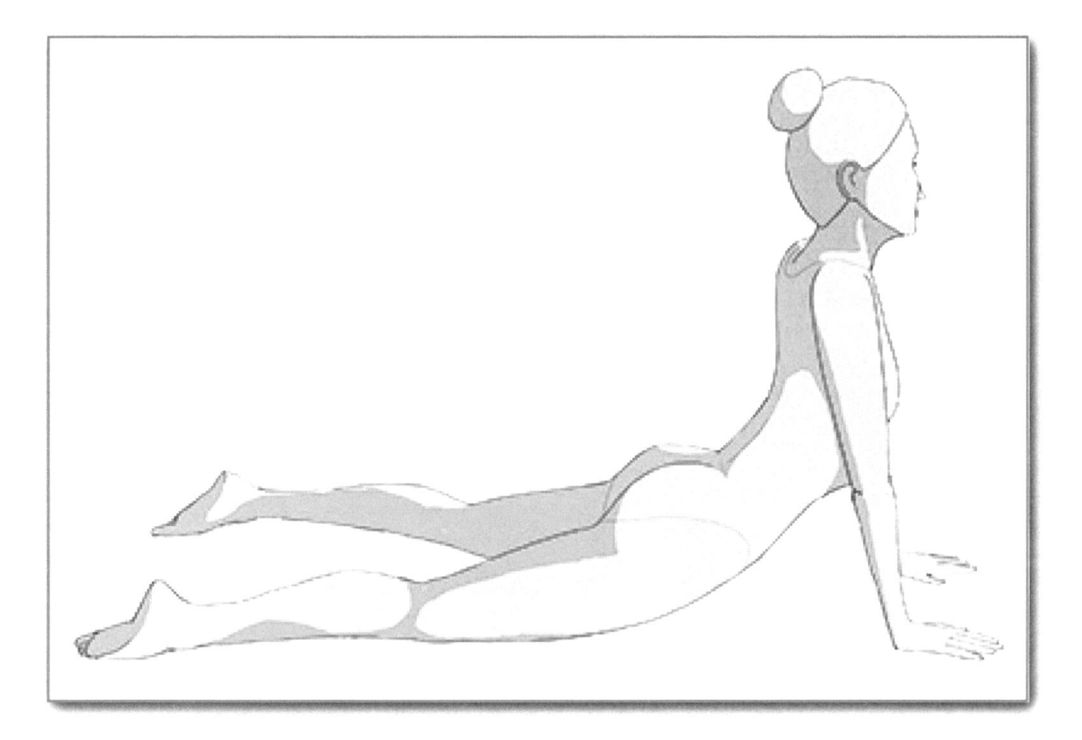

FIGURE 9.6: ABDOMINAL STRETCH

LOWER BODY

HAMSTRING STRETCH

Sit on the ground, with both legs straight out in front of you. Bend the left leg and place the sole of the left foot alongside the knee of the right leg. Allow the left leg to lie relaxed on the ground. Bend forward, keeping your back straight. You will feel the stretch in the hamstring of your right leg.

Repeat with your other leg.

QUAD STRETCH

Standing tall, hold onto a chair with your left hand, or place your left hand against the wall. Grab your right ankle with your right hand and bring the heel of your foot as close to your buttocks as you can, touching it, if possible. Relax.

Repeat with your other leg.

You can also complete this exercise lying down on your side.

FIGURE 9.7: QUAD STRETCH

CALF STRETCH

Standing tall, place both hands against the wall. Then place your right foot forward, bending the knee. Place your left leg further away from the wall, keeping your leg straight and your heel firmly on the ground. You will feel a stretch in the calf or lower part of your leg.

Repeat with your other leg.

FIGURE 9.8: CALF STRETCH

HIP FLEXOR STRETCH

Kneel down on your left knee and keep your right foot in front of your body. Keep your back straight throughout the exercise. Make sure that your right knee is behind your right toe at all times. Push your right knee forward slightly and lift your left knee off the ground. Hold the stretch position.

Repeat with your other leg.

FIGURE 9.9: HIP FLEXOR STRETCH

GLUTEAL STRETCH

Lie on the floor. Keep both knees bent and feet flat on the floor. Using your two hands, grab both knees and pull them toward your chest, as far as possible. Hold this position and then relax.

You can also complete this exercise using one leg at a time.

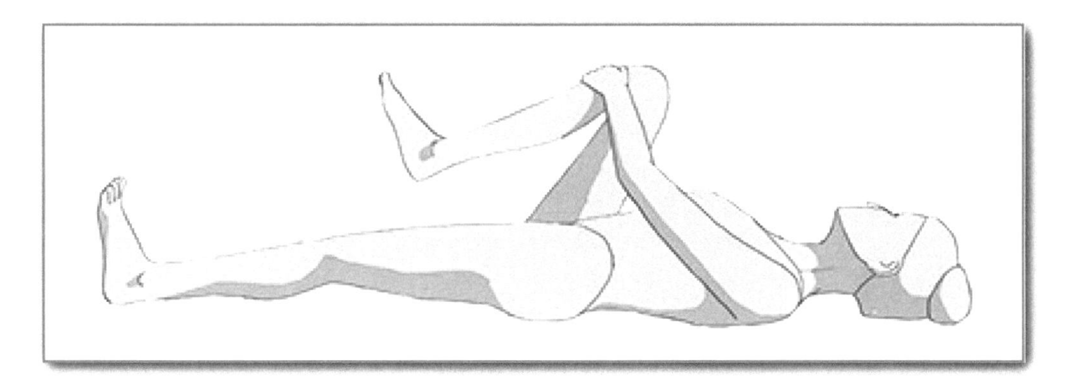

FIGURE 9.10: GLUTEAL STRETCH

ANKLE STRETCH

Sit on the floor and keep your back straight. Keep your right leg fully extended and keep your left knee bent, with your left foot flat against your knee. Using a towel or resistance band, wrap it around your right foot. Keeping your leg fully extended, pull the towel or resistance band toward your chest, using both hands. Hold the stretch and then relax.

Repeat with your other foot or ankle.

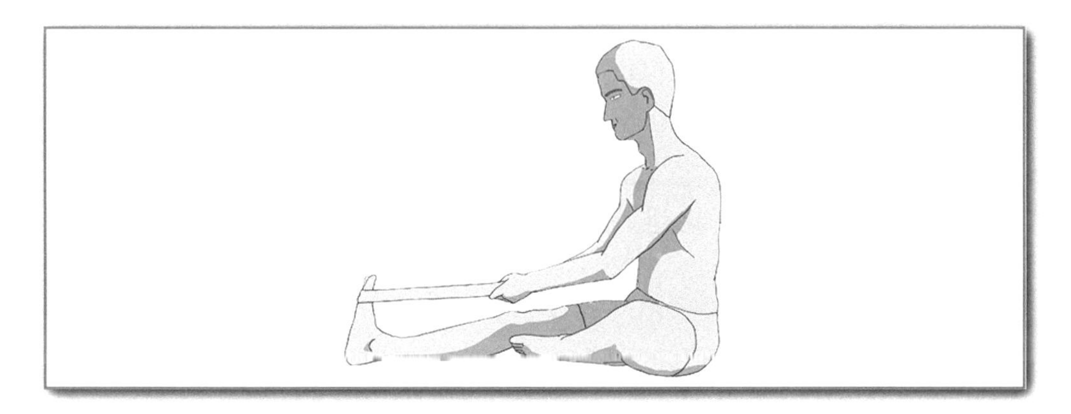

FIGURE 9.11: ANKLE STRETCH

HOW MUCH SHOULD I STRETCH?

Every dancer is different. Some dancers have good mobility and poor stability, while others are the opposite. In other words, dancers with good stability will have tight bodies resulting in dense connective tissue. Their muscles will have less elasticity and this means they have a smaller joint range of motion. These dancers have to focus on improving their flexibility more than their strength. Dancers who have good mobility and poor stability should focus more on improving their strength, rather than trying to increase their flexibility. Dancers with a larger range of motion and poor stability are more vulnerable to injuries such as strains or sprains.

It is important not to compare yourself with other dancers. Do not focus on how often another dancer stretches and the time they spend doing it. They may need to stretch more than you. Seek advice from a health professional if you are unsure which category you fall into. You will find that some dancers will have good stability and mobility, but usually there will always be one that you will have to work on more than the other.

THE BENEFITS OF EACH STRETCH ROUTINE

Deciding how often to stretch can be confusing. The benefits gained from a single stretch routine could last less than one hour. However, continuing to perform a multiweek stretch programme can benefit you for weeks after you have discontinued your stretch routine. To maintain your current flexibility, stretching once per week is sufficient. In order to increase your flexibility, ideally you will need to stretch more than once weekly, but no more than three times per week. When stretching each muscle group, it is sufficient to do up to three repetitions, with each lasting 30 seconds. You will not benefit from doing any more in each stretch session.

STRETCHING IN A NUTSHELL

DO

- Use your full range of motion.
- Complete at least one stretch for each muscle group.
- Hold each stretch for 30 seconds and no longer.
- Complete up to three repetitions for each stretch.
- Perform a stretch routine once weekly to maintain flexibility and up to three times per week to improve flexibility.
- Breathe deeply when performing the stretches, keeping your body and muscles relaxed.

DO NOT

- Forget to stretch opposing muscles, for example, stretching the quads and not stretching the hamstrings.
- Compare yourself to other dancers when either deciding on a stretch routine, or on how often you should stretch.
- 'Bounce' on the stretch causing the muscle to shorten and lengthen repeatedly.
- Force the stretch.
- Stretch if you feel any pain or discomfort.
- Hold your breath, when stretching.

CHAPTER 10
CONDITIONING FOR IRISH DANCERS

If a dancer cannot perform specific dance movements in accordance with the teacher's expectations, then almost immediately it is assumed that he or she is not doing it correctly. It is based on the belief that either he or she is simply not able to perform or not strong enough. What may not be fully understood, is that what appears to be a lack of strength or ability may actually be inefficient technique due to poor alignment, muscle imbalances or lack of flexibility. As time goes on, the more training the dancer does, the stronger he or she will become. However, if the dancer continues to train with alignment, muscle imbalance and flexibility shortcomings, then the end result will remain unchanged. In order for the dancer to break the cycle, new training patterns must be introduced to help improve their alignment, imbalances, flexibility and more importantly reducing the risk of injury. Begin by following these simple tips:

› Do not waste time practising bad habits simply because they are easier. The more this happens, the harder they are to undo. Become familiar with using proper techniques and form, whilst correcting body alignment.

› Think positively. Imagine how you will dance. Visualise how you will perform your next 'lift', gliding across the stage effortlessly, keeping your leg fully extended, your spine braced, your arms by your side, your head up and feeling confident. Eventually you will train your mind and your body to do just that. Your thoughts must support your goals if you want to achieve them.

› Increase your flexibility. Make sure you know exactly how you should be stretching and what muscles you need to focus on most. This will lead to good flexibility, with a more balanced approach.

- Make sure that the strength training routine you are following supports your needs. Also, ensure you complete the exercises in a balanced fashion and that they apply specifically to Irish dancing.

- All elements of conditioning, including alignment, balance, flexibility, strength training and cardiovascular training, must be interrelated. Each one of them must be trained to achieve the same outcome. For example, if your strength training routine results in building mass and weight, making you slower, and your cardiovascular training routine includes sprints to make you faster, then these two elements are not being trained to attain the same result.

SPECIFIC CONDITIONING

You will read books or articles that will tell you that dancers, in general, should only focus on certain elements of fitness rather than others. I strongly disagree, and instead believe that every athlete, regardless of their sport, should consider all elements of fitness when designing a training programme. A dancer's strength and conditioning has a huge impact on his or her development. Underdevelopment can result when some elements of fitness are ignored. The onus is on dance teachers and parents to develop their knowledge and learn the importance of including all elements of fitness in their training regime, or alternatively to seek advice from a highly qualified fitness professional. In short, the golden rule when designing a strength and conditioning programme for any athlete is to make it specific to the sport, while still including all elements of fitness.

If you want to increase your dance strength, then you must use strength movements that are similar to the dance steps you have to perform.

For example, to increase strength for a 'high click' you must consider the following:

SPEED

Fast.

MAIN MUSCLE GROUP

Hip flexors.

MAIN MUSCLE ACTION

Hip flexion.

Therefore, performing an isometric exercise for the hip flexors is out of the question when developing the 'high click', as it requires movement. However, a straight leg raise exercise can be included. As a dancer, parent or dance teacher you are not expected to know this information unless you have a strength and conditioning qualification. I am providing you with this knowledge to help you understand how a conditioning programme is designed specifically for Irish dancers.

Like any conditioning programme, you should begin slowly and then increase the intensity when the body is ready. The intensity you choose must match the strength and conditioning gains of the muscle.

EXAMPLES OF INTENSITY EXERCISES

You can increase the intensity of your strength training by advancing the exercise. A resistance band or light weight can also be used, depending on the exercise.

You can increase the intensity of your cardiovascular training by trying more difficult routines, steps or balance exercises. Anything that increases muscle activity will lead to improved performance, when done correctly.

AEROBIC FITNESS

Normally a routine dance class would not make a great impact on an Irish dancer's aerobic capacity. Therefore, in order to improve it, he or she must perform a separate workout that requires the body to make a great effort to bring about adaptation from within. An elevation in heart rate to approximately 70–80% of the maximum levels, maintained for 20–30 minutes is sufficient. Continuous activities such as swimming, running, skipping and five-a-side soccer are all examples of aerobic exercises. Performing an aerobic activity 1–3 times per week, depending on the training phase, is required. As a result of this, you as a dancer will be able to perform longer at a moderate maximum heart rate before becoming fatigued.

ANAEROBIC FITNESS

Anaerobic training involves huge outbursts of energy over a short period of time. To improve your anaerobic fitness, you must work at an 85–95% maximum heart rate, 2–5 times per week, depending on your training phase. Each effort can gradually increase from 10–50 seconds. In order to make this type of training works effectively, you must ensure that you make a 100% effort, both mentally and physically, to reach the prescribed times at each interval. Activities such as sprinting, jumps and skipping can all improve anaerobic fitness. As you progress, you as a dancer will be able to perform dancing techniques that require maximum effort, and you will be able to recover quickly.

Each anaerobic training phase usually lasts 4–8 weeks. You will complete 2–3 anaerobic workouts each week, giving yourself a rest day in between each one (see Table 10.1 below for further details). You will see on the 'sample training plan', outlined later in this chapter, that your first anaerobic training will begin during the 'specific preparation' training phase.

TABLE 10.1

ANAEROBIC TRAINING, PHASES 1–3

PHASE 1

WORKOUT 1

DISTANCE	QUANTITY	REST
100m sprints	7	2 minutes
200m sprints	5	2 minutes

WORKOUT 2

DISTANCE	QUANTITY	REST
200m sprints	7	2 minutes
400m sprints	3	2 minutes

WORKOUT 3

DISTANCE	QUANTITY	REST
400m sprints	5	2 minutes

PHASE 2

WORKOUT 1

DISTANCE	QUANTITY	REST
100m sprints	5	90 seconds
200m sprints	3	90 seconds
400m sprints	2	90 seconds
800m sprints	1	90 seconds

WORKOUT 2

DISTANCE	QUANTITY	REST
50m sprints	10	90 seconds
100m sprints	7	90 seconds
200m sprints	3	90 seconds

WORKOUT 3

DISTANCE	QUANTITY	REST
100m sprints	5	90 seconds
200m sprints	3	90 seconds

PHASE 3

WORKOUT 1

DISTANCE	QUANTITY	REST
400m sprints	4	60 seconds

WORKOUT 2

DISTANCE	QUANTITY	REST
100m sprints	5	60 seconds
200m sprints	3	60 seconds
400m sprints	2	60 seconds

WORKOUT 3

DISTANCE	QUANTITY	REST
400m sprints	5	60 seconds

PLYOMETRIC TRAINING

Constant jumping is required for most Irish dancing performances. Plyometric training (also known as jump training) has proven to be very effective for almost all of my Irish dancing clients to date. However, it can have a negative effect and cause injury if it is not approached in a gradual and systematic manner. You must ensure that you follow the steps outlined below (see Table 10.2) and only include plyometric training in your programme during the correct training phases (check the sample training plan, Table 10.3, further on in this chapter to see the training phases).

TABLE 10.2: PLYOMETRIC TRAINING PROGRAMME

LEVEL	EXERCISE	INTENSITY
Beginner	Squat jumps, plyometric	Low
Beginner or intermediate	Forward hops on a single leg or both legs over 20 metres. Complete five sets.	Low or medium
Intermediate	Double leg step jumps or hurdle jumps. Do 12 repetitions with each leg.	Medium
Intermediate or advanced	Single leg step jumps or hurdle jumps. Do 12 repetitions with each leg. Complete three sets.	High
Advanced	Single leg step jumps or hurdle jumps. Do 12 repetitions with each leg. Complete three sets.	High

BALANCING YOUR MUSCLES

Even after years of dancing, you will still continue to find muscle imbalances. Why? Because your steps require you to use certain muscle groups more than others. For example, the first thing you do as a dancer is point your toes. This is a non-stop action required in Irish dancing and is performed with minimal effort. The muscles used to perform this movement become very strong and it results in weak opposing muscles. You must make sure that the opposing muscles get attention when planning your strength training routine.

PLANNING A CONDITIONING PROGRAMME

You can use this simple system to guide you in order to ensure that your conditioning programme is progressive. This system is known as periodisation.

HOW DOES PERIODISATION TRAINING WORK?

Periodisation training is a change from high volume, low intensity nonsport-specific training to low volume, high intensity sports-specific training. This is carried out over a period of time, depending on the athlete's schedule.

As you know, your dancing year is divided into phases. These include: training for a big competition such as the World Irish Dancing Championships; taking part in a Feis every weekend; going on holidays or taking a few week's break; or a scheduled season break for up to eight weeks. These different phases in your dancing career will impact on your training schedule. You must ensure that the training phase you are pursuing suits your dancing schedule.

TRAINING PHASES

PREPARATION

The initial phase is usually the longest and occurs when there are no competitions or dance-specific training sessions scheduled. The main aim during this phase is to achieve a basic level of conditioning. This helps to prepare the dancer for more advanced workouts in the future. The general goals of the preparation phase include:

- Improving all aspects of fitness
- Improving technique
- Improving performance

SPECIFIC PREPARATION

This phase is a continuation of the preparation phase, where you begin by focusing on more dance-specific training. Example exercises include:

- Step drills

- New dance steps
- Dance-specific techniques

PRE-COMPETITION

Precompetition occurs between the preparation and the competition phases. During this stage, you will focus on maintaining fitness that has been developed throughout the preparation phase. You will also increase the intensity and decrease the volume.

The main aims during this phase are as follows:

- To maintain fitness levels including cardiovascular, strength, balance and flexibility.
- To maintain the dance-specific skills developed, for example, new steps.
- To practice, improve and perfect dancing techniques.

During this phase, there is an increased emphasis on dancing techniques, with less attention paid to fitness development training. However, you must always include a strength and conditioning training programme in your current regime.

COMPETITION PHASE (MAINTENANCE PHASE)

This phase is between the precompetition and postcompetition phases. During this stage, you will be constantly performing at Irish dancing competitions on a weekly or fortnightly basis. You should be well-conditioned going into this phase, with all of the hard work completed. You will also focus on maintaining the strength, power, aerobic, anaerobic and flexibility gains that you have developed during the previous phases.

POST-COMPETITION (TRANSITION AND ACTIVE REST)

This is a time for physical and mental recovery. It gives the dancer a chance to refresh and prepare mentally for the next big event. In the next section, I will explain in detail the importance of resting periods and what they involve.

RESTING PERIODS

Note that you must include rest periods throughout this periodisation programme, otherwise you could eventually overtrain, resulting in injury. Every dancer should include breaks of 2–3 weeks, at least 2–3 times each year. This rest time allows your body to recuperate and it allows you to refocus on your training and your programming. During this time, it is recommended that you stop dancing altogether and simply do some light conditioning training, if you so wish. If you overtrain your body, it can take a lot longer to recover and recuperate, requiring longer rest periods. Therefore, it is advisable to rest regularly.

The main aims during the rest period are to:

- Prevent weight gain. You do not want to lose the gains that we have achieved during the precompetition phase, so it is important to do other activities outside of dancing to maintain this progress, to some degree.
- Maintain aerobic fitness levels by performing low intensity workouts.
- Maintain strength by focusing on endurance, strength and power.
- Repair injuries and recuperate.

TABLE 11.1

YOUR SAMPLE TRAINING PLAN

SUBJECT	TRANSITION AND ACTIVE REST 2–4 WEEKS	PREPARATION PHASE 8 WEEKS	SPECIFIC PREPARATION 8 WEEKS	PRECOMPETITION PHASE 12 WEEKS	COMPETITION (MAINTENANCE) PHASE 12--18 WEEKS
STRENGTH TRAINING	Twice per week Low to moderate intensity 50–75% 1RM 3–6 sets 10–20 reps	Three times per week High intensity 80–90% 1RM 3–5 sets 4–8 reps	2–3 times per week High intensity 75–90% 1RM 3–5 sets 2–5 reps	1–2 times per week Very high intensity 90%> 1RM 1–3 sets 1–3 reps	Twice per week Moderate intensity 80–85% 1RM 2–3 sets 6–8 reps
AEROBIC CONDITIONING	Introduce physical activities with other sports, that are non-dance related.	Continuous activity 70–80% Max HR for 30 minutes, 3 times per week	Activity 70–80% Max HR for 30 minutes, 1–2 times per week.	Activity 70–80% Max HR for 30 minutes, once per week.	None
ANAEROBIC CONDITIONING	None	None	Interval training 85–95% Max HR 2–3 times per week	Interval training 95% Max HR 3–5 times per week	Interval training 95% Max HR 3–4 times per week
PLYOMETRICS	None	None	1–2 times per week	1–2 times per week	Once per week
FLEXIBILITY	3–4 times per week, pre and post exercise stretching.	3–4 times per week, pre and post exercise stretching.	3–4 times per week, pre and post exercise stretching.	3–4 times per week, pre and post exercise stretching.	3–4 times per week, pre and post exercise stretching.
OTHER	Review your last performances. Develop goals for next season.	Set goals. Mark your calendar year plan. Learn new steps. Improve your nutrition plan. Do balance training.	Improve your dancing technique. Focus on nutrition and balance training. Introduce sport psychology skills.	Refine choreography. Design new dancing dress. Focus on nutrition, balance training and sport psychology skills.	Focus on improving steps. Get pre and post-event nutritional knowledge. Use sport psychology skills. Keep performing balance exercises.

NOTE: HR = HEART RATE – 1RM = 1 REPETITION MAXIMUM

TABLE 12.1
SEASON 2015 – SAMPLE YEAR CALENDAR

MONTH	COMPETITION	TRAINING PHASE	DURATION
January		Preparation phase	
February		Precompetition phase	
March		Competition phase	
April	World Championships	Competition phase	
May	National	Competition phase	
June		Transition and active	
July		Preparation phase	
August		Specific preparation	
September		Precompetition phase	
October	All-Ireland	Competition phase	
November	Oireachtas	Competition phase	
December		Transition phase and active rest	

STILL UNSURE AS
TO WHAT YOU SHOULD BE FOCUSING ON?

By now, you should have a good understanding of how planning a training programme works. You may still be asking questions about what exercises you should be focusing on. Obviously, you will not be able to do all of the exercises outlined! In this book, I have not included any sample training programmes, and I have done this on purpose. Why? Every dancer is different, each with differing strengths and weaknesses. This means that the same dance-specific programme will not benefit all dancers. In this situation it is always advisable to seek some direction from a health and fitness professional, with knowledge of the activity. You can get specific programme information by visiting my website:

– www.irishdancingphysicalfitness.com.

I will personally design a training programme to best suit your needs and update it, when necessary.

CONCLUSION

Now that you are at the end of the book, I hope that you have learned something from the information I have provided you with and that it will help you to become the best dancer you can be.

MAXINE SPELMAN

Remember, by giving it 100% already makes you a winner!

Best of luck with your dancing career and maybe I will see you in the future.

CONTACT INFORMATION

If you have any questions, please do not hesitate to contact me personally.

Facebook page: Irish Dancing Physical Fitness

Website: www.irishdancingphysicalfitness.com

I look forward to hearing from you.

Peter O'Grady

Designed, typeset, printed and bound in Ireland by

PubliBook Ireland
www.publibookireland.com